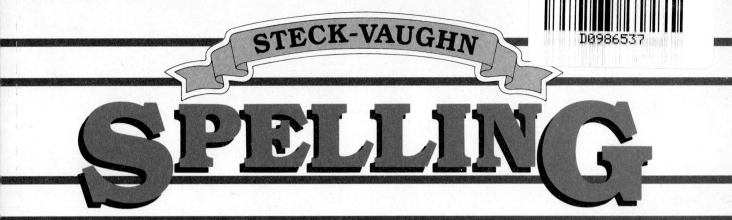

SPELLING
STECK-VAUGHN

JOHN R. PESCOSOLIDO, Ph.D.
Visiting Professor
University of Hartford
West Hartford, Connecticut

Consultants

Betty Dotson
Supervisor of Language Arts K-12
Indianapolis Public Schools
Indianapolis, Indiana

Felice M. Rockoff
Reading Teacher
New York City Public Schools
New York, New York

Theodore J. Thibodeau
K-8 Curriculum Coordinator
Attleboro Public Schools
Attleboro, Massachusetts

Sister Sarah Page
Director of Curriculum and Instruction
Archdiocese of St. Louis
St. Louis, Missouri

Sister Margaret Sevier
Reading Consultant
Archdiocese of Philadelphia
Philadelphia, Pennsylvania

Anna L. Ulrich
Reading Language Arts Specialist
Albuquerque Public Schools
Albuquerque, New Mexico

Anita Uphaus
Instructional Coordinator
Austin Independent School District
Austin, Texas

STECK-VAUGHN
COMPANY

Supervising Editor: Kathleen Fitzgibbon

Project Coordinator: Cynthia Ellis

Design and Production: Kirchoff/Wohlberg, Inc.

Editorial Director: Mary Jane Martin

Editor: Kathleen Fischer

Writers: Patricia Crittenden (pp. 102, 108, 120); Linda Ekblad (pp. 88, 166, 190); Carol Ellis (pp. 30, 62, 114, 134, 152, 158); Bernice Golden (p. 18); Roberta Green (pp. 94, 140); Bobbi Katz (p. 184); Phyllis Keaton (pp. 12, 24, 56, 76); Colleen Normandin (p. 70); Alice Pernick (p. 44); Julia Remine Piggin (pp. 82, 172); Stuart Podhaizer (Etymologies); Leslie Purificación (pp. 146, 178); Carole Ridolfino (p. 126); Joan Rosenblatt (p. 38); Lorraine Sotiriou (p. 50); Doreen Nation Ziobro (p. 6)

Artists: Maxie Chambliss (p. 44); Brian Cody (pp. 24, 25, 76, 77, 166); Diane Dawson (Checkpoint pages); Betsy Day (pp. 102, 103); Arlene Dubanevich (pp. 18, 19); Jon Friedman (pp. 82, 140, 141, 178, 179); John Gamache (pp. 70, 71); Jon Goodell (pp. 134, 135, 172, 173); Konrad Hack (pp. 30, 31, 146); Meryl Henderson (pp. 38, 39, 94, 95, 114, 115); Ruth Hoffman (pp. 184, 185); True Kelley (pp. 88, 89, Language Arts and Wrap Up pages); Elizabeth Koda-Callan (Alphabet art); Dora Leder (pp. 62, 63, 152, 153); Tom Leonard (pp. 3, 35, 56, 57, 67, 99, 131, 163, 195, 196, 224); Susan Lexa (p. 190); Jan Pyk (p. 50); Jerry Smath (Spelling Dictionary); Arthur Thompson (p. 126); John Wallner (pp. 6, 108, 109, 158, 159); Lane Yerkes (pp. 12, 13)

Cover Art: Maxie Chambliss

ISBN: 0-8114-4105-9

9 0 DP 97 96 95

Contents

Lesson 1   Words with /ă/

Listen for /ă/ as you say each word.

ask

matter

black

add

match

Saturday

class

apple

subtract

thank

catch

January

after

hammer

half

laugh

1. Write four words that begin with the vowel sound /ă/.

_____

_____

2. Write two words that end with the sound /f/.

_____

3. Write three words that end with the sound /k/.

_____

_____

4. Write two words that end with the last four letters of <u>hatch</u>.

_____

5. Write two words that are always spelled with a capital letter.

_____

6. Write the word that ends with the letter <u>t</u>.

_____

7. Write five words that have double consonants.

dd _____   pp _____

ss _____   tt _____

mm _____

Checkpoint

Write a spelling word for each clue.
Then use the Checkpoint Study Plan on page 224.

1. A tool you use to hit a nail is a _hammer_

2. When someone tells a funny joke, you _laugh_

3. The color of coal is _black_

4. If there's a problem, ask, "What's the _matter_?"

5. To get the sum, you _add_

6. When a ball is thrown to you, you _catch_

7. A round, red fruit is an _apple_.

8. To take away from is to _subtract_

9. To question is to _ask_.

10. Students and a teacher are a _match_

11. You _thank_ someone for a gift.

12. It's not the whole thing, but _half_

13. The opposite of before is _after_.

14. The first month of the year is _January_

15. To make a fire use a _match_

16. This mystery word is very old. And it looked
    different long ago. It comes from two Old
    English words. The first is *Saeter*. The second
    is *daeg*. *Saeter* was the name of the Roman
    god Saturn. *Daeg* meant day. Say these two
    words together to give yourself a clue to the
    mystery word. ____

Use each word once to complete this story.

LATE AGAIN

R-r-ring. R-r-ring.

"Oh, no!" cried Robbie when the alarm clock rang. He had been dreaming about the tree house he was going to build. In the dream he had just picked up a nail and the _____ when the clock rang.

Robbie jumped out of bed. "I'll be late for school. What is the _____ with me?"

This would be the third time in the month of _____ that Robbie was late. His teacher would _____ him for a late pass. She might even keep him _____ school. And that would never do!

He got dressed so fast he didn't even see that his socks didn't _____ . He put on one brown sock and one _____ sock!

Robbie went to the kitchen. He drank _____ of a glass of milk. He took an _____ from the table. Then he ran to _____ the bus before his mother could stop him.

"The bus is so empty," he thought. He had forgotten to put on his watch. Robbie asked the bus driver for the time. He said it was nine o'clock. Robbie remembered to _____ the driver.

Then he remembered about the math test. Ms. Blue was giving the _____ a test today. She wanted to see if everyone knew how to _____ and _____ numbers. And Robbie had forgotten to study.

Finally Robbie got to school. To his surprise nobody was there. Robbie smiled. Then he began to _____ .

"Of course, no one is here," he said. "Today is _____ !"

Robbie hurried home so he could start building his tree house.

7

ask
matter
black
add
match
Saturday
class
apple
subtract
thank
catch
January
after
hammer
half
laugh

Alphabetical Order

When words are in <u>a</u>-<u>b</u>-<u>c</u> order, they are in alphabetical order. This group of words is in alphabetical order:

bend   friend   horse

This group of words is not in alphabetical order:

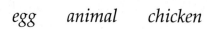

egg   animal   chicken

★ Put the following groups of words in alphabetical order.

1. add   January   hammer   **2. matter   half   class**

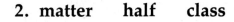

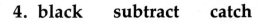

3. thank   ask   Saturday   **4. black   subtract   catch**

5. match   laugh   apple

8

Wrap Up

LESSON 1

AFTER THE TEST . . .

1. Did you spell all the words on your test correctly?

   If you did, go on to WRITE NOW! If you missed a word, it is important to know why.

2. Did you forget to cross a <u>t</u>?

   _____

3. Did you leave the letter <u>c</u> out of <u>subtract</u>? _____

4. Did you forget to capitalize the first letter of <u>January</u> or <u>Saturday</u>? _____

5. If you made some other mistake, what was it? _____

6. Write the words you missed.

   _____

   _____

NOW WHAT ?

It helps some people to hear a word spelled out loud. If you have trouble with some spelling words, it may be fun to try this.

Look at a word you missed while someone says it correctly. Close your eyes and try to see the word. With your eyes still closed, say the word and spell it out loud.

Open your eyes and write the word. Did you spell it correctly? Say it again while you look at it.

WRITE NOW!

Here are four more words with /ă/:

plants   fact   stand   glass

Use two of these words in a story about a strange plant made of glass. You might want to begin: It looked like a marble, but . . .

Lesson 2 Words with /ā/

Listen for /ā/ as you say each word.

ate

late

safe

page

face

save

place

came

change

gray

away

pay

May

break

great

April

1. Which two words begin with capital letters?

_____   _____

2. Write two words that have the letters <u>ate</u>.

_____   _____

3. Write four words that end with the last two letters of <u>say</u>.

_____   _____

_____   _____

4. Write the word that begins with /k/.

_____

5. Write two words in which you hear /j/ but do not see the letter <u>j</u>.

_____   _____

6. Which two words begin with the letter <u>s</u>?

_____   _____

7. Write two words in which you hear /s/ at the end but do not see the letter <u>s</u>.

_____   _____

8. In which two words is /ā/ spelled with the letters <u>ea</u>? _____   _____

9. Which two words have two syllables?

Checkpoint

Write a spelling word for each clue.
Then use the Checkpoint Study Plan on page 224.

1. Something that's terrific or wonderful is ____.

2. When you mix black and white, you get ____.

3. To rescue from danger is to ____.

4. If it's not near, it's far ____.

5. The fifth month of the year is ____.

6. Your eyes, nose, and mouth are on your ____.

7. If you don't stay the same, you ____.

8. Today you eat, yesterday you ____.

9. A certain spot is a ____.

10. To crack is to ____.

11. If it's not early, it's ____.

12. A tree has a leaf, a book has a ____.

13. The past tense of come is ____.

14. If it's not free, you must ____.

15. Where there's no danger, it is ____.

16. English has borrowed words from many other languages. The mystery word comes from the Latin word *aperilis*. *Aperilis* means "open." It names the time of year when flowers begin to open. Can you guess the word? ____

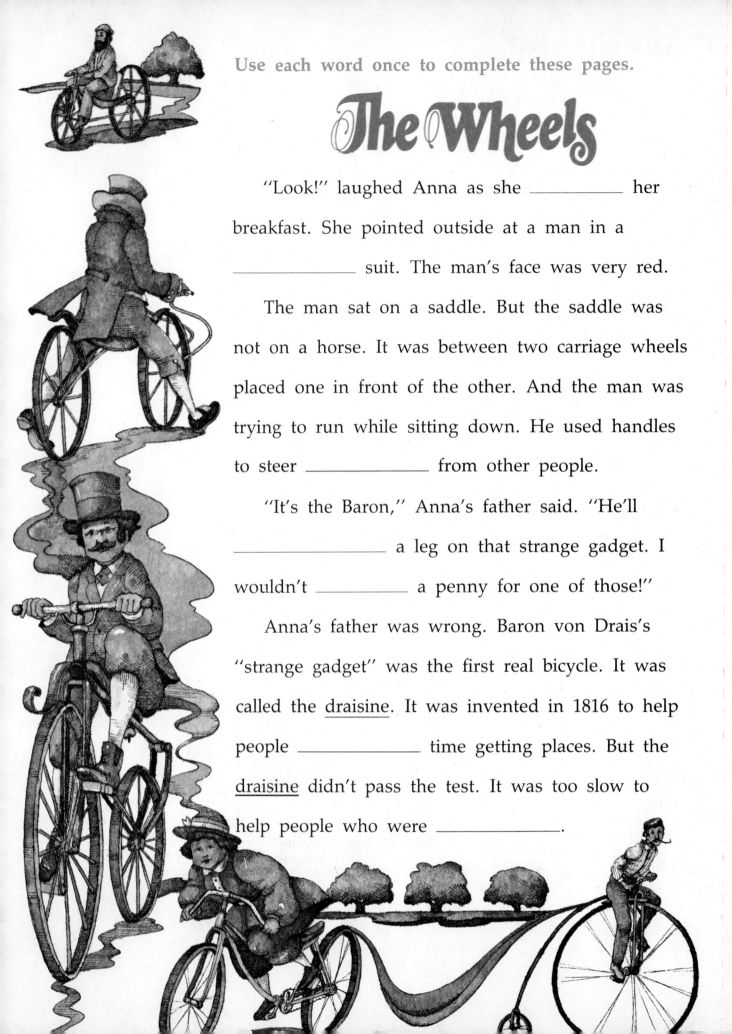

Use each word once to complete these pages.

The Wheels

"Look!" laughed Anna as she _____ her breakfast. She pointed outside at a man in a _____ suit. The man's face was very red.

The man sat on a saddle. But the saddle was not on a horse. It was between two carriage wheels placed one in front of the other. And the man was trying to run while sitting down. He used handles to steer _____ from other people.

"It's the Baron," Anna's father said. "He'll _____ a leg on that strange gadget. I wouldn't _____ a penny for one of those!"

Anna's father was wrong. Baron von Drais's "strange gadget" was the first real bicycle. It was called the draisine. It was invented in 1816 to help people _____ time getting places. But the draisine didn't pass the test. It was too slow to help people who were _____.

Many changes took _____. In 1839, a wonderful _____ was made. A man put pedals on his bicycle. Now a person could ride a bicycle with both feet off the ground. Macmillan's new bicycle turned a _____ in the bicycle history book.

In 1866, Pierre Lallement invented a new bicycle. It was called the boneshaker. That was a good name for it. If you were not careful, it would shake you up. You could fall flat on your _____! It was dangerous.

In 1869, the <u>Phantom</u> made its appearance. It was made of iron, not wood. It _____ with rubber tires. Best of all, it was _____. The days of the boneshaker had ended. Bicycles were becoming like the bikes we ride today. The Baron's "strange gadget" turned out to be a _____ idea.

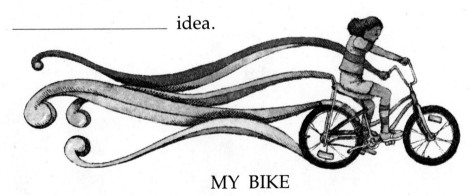

MY BIKE

The best month for riding my bike is _____, Because in _____ it rains every day!

ate
late
safe
page
face
save
place
came
change
gray
away
pay
May
break
great
April

Capitals and Periods

Begin the first word of a sentence with a capital letter.

My sister collects postage stamps.

Put a period (.) at the end of a sentence that tells or explains something. Most sentences end with a period.

The first postage stamp was made in England.

★ Write the story below using these spelling words. Correct capital letters and put periods where they belong.

**May   face   save   place   late
safe   page   gray   away**

heather likes to ___ stamps   she keeps them ___ in
a dry ___   she must keep them ___ from her new ___ puppy

last ___, Heather went to her stamp club   she went in the

morning   a ___ fell out of her stamp book before she left   she

looked all over the place for the page when she got home

   then she looked at her puppy   the hair on his ___ looked

stuck together   guess who had a ___ breakfast

14

AFTER THE TEST...

1. Did you spell all the words on your test correctly? _____
If you did, go on to WRITE NOW! If you missed a word, it is important to know why.

2. Did you forget the letter <u>e</u> at the end of a word? _____

3. Did you forget to capitalize the first letter of <u>April</u> or <u>May</u>? _____

4. Did you put letters in the wrong order? _____

5. If you made some other mistake, what was it? _____

6. Write the words you missed.

_____

NOW WHAT?

It helps some people to see a word written in a special way. If you have trouble with some words, it may be fun for you to try this.

Write the word. But write the vowels in green and write the consonants in red. Stare at the word. Close your eyes. Can you still see the word? Spell it with your eyes closed.

WRITE NOW!

Here are four more words with /ā/:
grade became later lay
Use one of these words to write a book title. For example: <u>The Chicken That Tried to Lay Square Eggs</u>.

15

Lesson 3   Words with /ā/

Listen for /ā/ as you say each word.

paint

rain

aid

wait

train

aim

sail

afraid

paper

danger

fable

able

table

weigh

eight

they

1. Write four words that end with /l/.

_____   _____

_____   _____

2. Write two words that end with the letters <u>er</u>.

_____   _____

3. Write two words in which /ā/ is spelled <u>ei</u>.

_____   _____

4. Which two words end with the last three letters of <u>pain</u>?

_____   _____

5. Write three words that begin with the sound /ā/.

_____   _____

6. Which two words begin with the letter <u>w</u>?

_____   _____

7. Write the word that begins with the letters <u>th</u>.

_____

8. Which word begins and ends like <u>point</u>?

_____

9. Which two words end with the letter <u>d</u>?

_____

Checkpoint

Write a spelling word for each clue.
Then use the Checkpoint Study Plan on page 224.

1. A story that teaches a lesson is a ____.

2. Something that falls but doesn't get hurt is ____.

3. If you could get hurt, you're in ____.

4. In a car you drive, on a boat you ____.

5. Another word for scared is ____.

6. When you eat dinner, you sit at the ____.

7. To help someone is to give him ____.

8. A group of connected railroad cars is a ____.

9. You count five, six, seven, ____.

10. A word that means stop is ____.

11. If you can do something, you are ____.

12. To point at something is to ____.

13. To find out how many pounds, you ____.

14. You write us and we, them and ____.

15. Coloring used to make pictures is ____.

16. Long ago in England, people wrote on tree bark. In China, people wrote on silk and bamboo. Around the Mediterranean Sea, people wrote on something called *papyrus. Papyrus* was made of dried grass. Today most people use another material to write on. It is made of finely cut wood. The name of this material comes from the word *papyrus.* This is the mystery word. Can you guess it? ____

The Happy Village

It's easy to make your own little village. You can make it with paper and paste.

To begin, spread pieces of paper on top of a desk or _____. Then tear more pieces of _____ into strips. Then mix one cup of flour with enough water to make paste. Use the tops of seven or _____ milk cartons for the buildings.

Wet a few strips of paper with water. Then coat the strips of paper with the paste. Don't be _____ to use a lot of paste. Wind the paper around a milk carton. You will be _____ to make any building shape by adding more paper.

Have a wet towel to _____ you when your hands become sticky. You should _____ to work for an hour. Then stop and _____ for the piece to dry before you paint.

Later, get a brush and _____ the building.

To make the ground, use the paste over crumpled newspaper. When dry, paint it green. Then paint a lake. Make a boat to _____ in the lake.

Your village needs a train station. Make a _____ using old matchboxes for the cars. Make the train tracks out of toothpicks. Buttons work well for train wheels because _____ are round and small.

You can add mountains and bridges. You can even add a sign to tell of _____, like "Falling Rocks" or "Bridge Out."

What is missing? People! There is a saying from an old _____."A village without people is like a fruit without taste." Make tiny clay people. If they don't _____ too much you might put them in your boat. They won't get wet. In your village, it will never _____.

paint
rain
aid
wait
train
aim
sail
afraid
paper
danger
fable
able
table
weigh
eight
they

Compound Words

When two words are used together as one word, the new word is a compound word.

base + *ball* makes the compound word *baseball*
chop + *sticks* makes the compound word *chopsticks*

⭐ Match a word in List A with a word in List B and write a compound word.

List A	List B	Compound Words
1. sail	weight	
2. paint	top	
3. paper	boat	
4. rain	box	
5. table	bow	
6. mail	brush	

⭐ Then write a sentence using each compound word you just made. Circle the compound word in each sentence.

7.

8.

9.

10.

11.

12.

20

LESSON 3

AFTER THE TEST . . .

1. Did you spell all the words on your test correctly? _____

   If you did, go on to WRITE NOW! If you missed a word, it is important to know why.

2. Did you forget to dot an <u>i</u>?

   _____

3. Did you put in an extra letter?

   _____

4. Did you write <u>way</u> instead of <u>weigh</u>? _____

5. If you made some other mistake, what was it? _____

6. Write the words you missed.

   _____

   _____

NOW WHAT ?

It helps some people to hear a word spelled out loud. If you have trouble with some spelling words, it may be fun for you to try this.

Start spelling the word with a whisper. Get louder as you say each letter. Do this until you can spell the word.

WRITE NOW!

Here are four more words with /ā/:

mail states weight obey

Use two of these words to write an ad about a special kind of pizza that helps people lose weight.

21

Lesson 4 Words with /ĕ/

Listen for /ĕ/ as you say each word.

dress

address

end

second

forget

spent

egg

next

help

test

head

read

ready

said

again

says

1. Write three words that have double consonants.

   gg _____   ss _____

   dd and ss _____

2. Which word begins and ends with the letter s?

   _____

3. Write two words in which ai spells /ĕ/.

   _____   _____

4. Write two words that end with the letters nd.

   _____   _____

5. Write three words in which ea spells /ĕ/.

   _____   _____

   _____

6. Which four words end with the letter t?

   _____   _____

   _____   _____

7. Which word ends with the letter p?

   _____

8. Write the word that ends with the letter y.

   _____

Checkpoint

Write a spelling word for each clue.
Then use the Checkpoint Study Plan on page 224.

1. I come right after you, so I'm ____ .

2. For breakfast you might eat an ____ .

3. I say, you say, he ____ .

4. If Eddie is all set to go, then Eddie is ____ .

5. The opposite of the beginning is the ____ .

6. To aid someone is to ____ .

7. If you used your money, your money is ____ .

8. "Once more" means ____ .

9. Next after first comes ____ .

10. The opposite of remember is ____ .

11. Something to wear is a ____ .

12. The past tense of say is ____ .

13. Mail is sent to your ____ .

14. This is the best book I have ____ .

15. Another word for quiz or exam is ____ .

16. Do you know what raining cats and dogs means? It means that it's raining heavily. A phrase like raining cats and dogs is called an idiom. You may know what each word of an idiom means. But that won't tell you what the whole idiom means. To keep one's ____ means to stay calm. To lose one's ____ means to lose one's calm. What is the mystery word? ____

23

ME-2

Use each word once to complete this story.

ME-2 was a little robot with a big problem. She had a very bad memory.

Friday morning ME-2 ate bread and a scrambled _____ . Then she forgot that she had eaten breakfast. So she ate it _____ .

On Saturday she put on blue jeans. Then she forgot what she was wearing. So she put on her best _____ , too.

Things were bad at home. And they were no better at school. When ME-2 remembered her reading book, she forgot what she had _____ . When she remembered her math _____ , she forgot to study. And she was never _____ for gym because she always forgot her sneakers.

One day ME-2 forgot where she lived. She had forgotten her own _____ . So ME-2 _____ the night with her best friend, US-2. Her mother was very worried. She found ME-2 at school the very _____ day. Mother _____ , "This won't happen a _____ time. You are going to go to the doctor."

24

The doctor gave ME-2 a checkup. Soon it was over. ME-2 told her mother, "The doctor _____ I'm just fine. I wish I could remember why you brought me here."

"Doctor, how can ME-2 be fine?" asked her mother. "She would lose her _____ if it was not screwed on her shoulders! Can't you _____ her?"

Her words gave the doctor an idea. The doctor looked at the screws in ME-2's head. Sure enough! One screw was loose. She fixed it. That put an _____ to ME-2's bad memory.

"Oh, no! I just remembered something," cried ME-2. "We get report cards tomorrow. That is something I wish I could _____!"

25

Entry Words and Entries

An entry word in a dictionary tells how a word is spelled. An entry word is printed in dark, heavy letters. The entry comes next. It gives more information about the word. Many words have more than one meaning. Different meanings are numbered.

> **read·y** | rĕd′ē | — *adjective* **readier,**
> **readiest 1.** Prepared for action or use: *Are you ready to go? Dinner is ready.* **2.** Willing: *I'm ready to listen to your idea.* **3.** About to do something; likely: *She looked like she was ready to cry.* **4.** Quick; prompt and alert: *She has a ready answer for everything.* **5.** Easy to get at; close at hand: *You should always have some ready money.*

★ Answer these questions about the dictionary entry above.

1. What is the entry word in the example above? _____

2. How many meanings does this word have? _____

★ Write the following words in alphabetical order. Then look them up in the Spelling Dictionary. Write the page on which the entry appears. Then write the number of meanings each word has.

egg   next   address   help

Word	Page	Number of Meanings
3.		
4.		
5.		
6.		

Wrap Up

LESSON 4

AFTER THE TEST...

1. Did you spell all the words on your test correctly? _____

   If you did, go on to WRITE NOW! If you missed a word, it is important to know why.

2. Did you forget to double the <u>d</u> or <u>s</u> in <u>address</u>? _____

3. Did you leave out a letter in <u>again</u>? _____

4. Did you put letters in the wrong order? _____

5. If you made some other mistake, what was it? _____

6. Write the words you missed.

   _____

   _____

   _____

NOW WHAT ?

It helps some people to see a word in a special way. If you have trouble with some spelling words, it may be fun for you to try this.

Write a word on colored paper with chalk. Look at it. Say each letter until you can spell the word. Erase it and write another. When you finish, you will have a lovely picture!

WRITE NOW!

Here are four more words with /ĕ/:

left less letter chest

Use two of these words in a story about a hidden treasure. You might begin: I was helping Aunt Liz clean her attic.

27

Lesson 5   Plurals

Say each word.

clowns

trains

tests

eggs

hammers

paints

hands

papers

tables

places

pages

apples

classes

addresses

dresses

matches

Complete the word equations.

1. test   +   s   = _____

2. egg   +   s   = _____

3. train   +   s   = _____

4. hand   +   s   = _____

5. paint   +   s   = _____

6. clown   +   s   = _____

7. paper   +   s   = _____

8. hammer   +   s   = _____

9. page   +   s   = _____

10. table   +   s   = _____

11. place   +   s   = _____

12. apple   +   s   = _____

13. class   +   es = _____

14. dress   +   es = _____

15. match   +   es = _____

16. address +   es = _____

Checkpoint

Write a spelling word for each clue.
Then use the Checkpoint Study Plan on page 224.

1. Fruits that grow on trees are ____ .

2. Pieces of clothing are ____ .

3. Letters in the mail have names and ____ .

4. Things to write on are ____ .

5. Circus people who make you laugh are ____ .

6. The woods and the sea are different ____ .

7. You catch a basketball with your ____ .

8. A book is made up of many ____ .

9. Make a picture of a rainbow with many ____ .

10. Things that run on railroad tracks are ____ .

11. Hens lay, and you might eat, ____ .

12. Are you taking one class or two ____?

13. Things you use to start fires are ____ .

14. Tools you use with nails are ____ .

15. The teacher will mark your ____ .

16. This mystery word comes from the Latin word
tabula. A *tabula* was a board or plank. It was
often used for writing or playing games. The
mystery word that comes from *tabula* names
something we set our food on or play games
on. Can you guess it? Add <u>s</u> to this word.
What do you get? ____

JOHN HENRY

Use each word once to complete these pages.

All the people in the South knew about John Henry. They said he could swing a hammer so fast that you could hear thunder behind it. John Henry didn't go to _____ to learn how to swing a hammer. People said he was born with a hammer in his hand.

John Henry spent all of his time hammering steel spikes for the trains. He followed the _____ all over. He lived at many different _____ .

People will never forget the day John Henry raced a machine. It was one of the biggest _____ of his power. People came from _____ far away to see if John Henry could beat a machine. The women wore bright

_____ . Men wore their best shirts. They brought picnics of fresh bread and _____ . There were _____ for dessert. They sat on blankets or at picnic _____ .

The contest began. Who would win? Wham! Wham! John Henry was fast. But the machine was faster than John Henry.

"Bring me two _____ !" he cried. With hammers in both _____ , he was as fast as any machine. The hammers got very hot. Soon they started to glow. They were like _____ .

"Look!" a woman shouted. "John Henry is winning."

It was true. The smoke was gone. The people saw that the man had beaten the machine.

John Henry isn't in the _____ of your history book. But people in the South still talk about the greatest steel-driver of them all.

A. clown + clown = _____

B. paint + paint = _____

C. paper + paper = _____

31

clowns
trains
tests
eggs
hammers
paints
hands
papers
tables
places
pages
apples
classes
addresses
dresses
matches

Base Words

A word from which other words are formed is called a base word.

The base word for <u>places</u> is <u>place</u>.
The base word for <u>tests</u> is <u>test</u>.

⭐ Write the following words in alphabetical order. Then write the base word for each word.

classes   eggs   addresses   hands

<u>Words</u>   <u>Base Words</u>

1. _____   _____

2. _____   _____

3. _____   _____

4. _____   _____

In a dictionary, many entry words are base words. To find the word <u>matches</u>, look up the base word <u>match</u>. To find the word <u>papers</u>, look up the base word <u>paper</u>.

Different forms of each base word may be listed in the definition. The different forms are printed in dark letters.

> **clown** | kloun | — *noun, plural* **clowns 1.** A person who has a job, usually with a circus, doing tricks and telling jokes to make people laugh: *a circus clown.* **2.** A person who is always making jokes or acting foolishly: *the class clown.—verb* **clowned, clowning 1.** To perform as a clown in a circus or show: *The chimpanzees clowned in the center ring of the circus.* **2.** To behave like a clown: *My friend clowns around too much.*

⭐ Look at the dictionary entry above.

5. What is the base word? _____

6. What different forms are printed in dark letters?

_____

LESSON 5

AFTER THE TEST . . .

1. Did you spell all the words on

   your test correctly? _____
   If you did, go on to WRITE NOW! If you missed a word, it is important to know why.

2. Did you forget to write <u>es</u> after words that end with <u>ss</u> or <u>ch</u>?

   _____

3. Did you leave out a letter?

   _____

4. Did you write a capital letter when you shouldn't have?

   _____

5. If you made some other mistake,

   what was it? _____

6. Write the words you missed.

   _____

   _____

NOW WHAT ?

It helps some people to hear a word spelled with rhythm. If you have trouble with some spelling words, it may be fun for you to try this.

If the word ends with <u>es</u>, tap your right foot as you spell the word out loud. If the word ends with <u>s</u>, tap your left foot as you spell the word out loud.

WRITE NOW!

Here are four more words that end with <u>s</u> or <u>es</u>:

heads   glasses   cakes   grapes

Use two of these words to write a recipe for your own special grape cake or grape drink.

Lesson 6   Words in Review

A. catch

    half

    laugh

B. place

    gray

    break

    April

C. afraid

    danger

    weigh

    they

D. address

    second

    ready

    again

    says

★ Use a piece of paper for the starred activities.

1. In Lesson 1 you studied two ways to spell /ă/: **a, au.** Write the words in list A.

2. In Lesson 2 you studied four ways to spell /ā/: **a_e, ay, ea, a.** Write the words in list B.

★3. Write the review words from lists A and B in alphabetical order.

4. In Lesson 3 you studied four ways to spell /ā/: **ai, a, ei, ey.** Write the words in list C.

5. In Lesson 4 you studied four ways to spell /ĕ/: **e, ea, ai, ay.** Write the words in list D.

★6. Now write a sentence for each review word in lists C and D.

★7. Write the review words in lists C and D in alphabetical order.

34

Proof It Yourself

The sentences below have been proofread. The proofreading marks
tell you what mistakes have to be corrected.

- *sp* means that the word is misspelled.
- = means that a letter should be a capital.

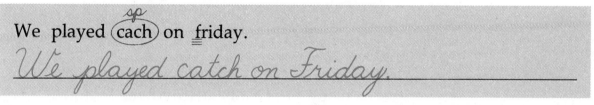

We played (cach) on friday.

We played catch on Friday.

Write the sentences correctly. Use each sentence to begin a paragraph.
Write each paragraph on another paper. Proofread your work.

1. Last saturday I saw something that made me (laff).

   _____

   _____

2. there is a (grate) new park on grove rd.

   _____

   _____

3. Most people are (afrade) of nancy's dog, but I'm not.

   _____

   _____

4. i can't wait to see our team play yorkville (agen).

   _____

   _____

5. all the (clases) in our school liked mr. magic's show.

   _____

   _____

Lesson 7   Words with /ĕ/

Listen for /ĕ/ as you say each word.

best

better

cents

February

never

kept

sent

September

slept

them

then

Wednesday

when

friend

many

guess

1. Which three words end with the letters <u>er</u>?

_____

_____

2. Which word begins with the letter <u>m</u>?

_____

3. In which two words do you see two vowels together but hear only one vowel sound?

_____

4. Which two words begin with the letters <u>th</u>?

_____

5. Which three words are always spelled with a capital letter? _____

_____

6. Write the word that begins with the letters <u>wh</u>.

_____

7. Which four words begin with /s/?

_____

_____

8. Write two words that end with the last three letters of <u>swept</u>.

_____

9. Which word ends with the letters <u>st</u>?

Checkpoint

Write a spelling word for each clue.
Then use the Checkpoint Study Plan on page 224.

1. The opposite of few is ___.

2. "Not ever" means ___.

3. Valentine's Day is in ___.

4. The past tense of send is ___.

5. Someone you know and like is your ___.

6. When you don't know the answer, try to ___.

7. "Held on to and saved" means ___.

8. School starts in ___.

9. Tonight you'll sleep, last night you ___.

10. The finest is the ___.

11. You ask what, why, where, and ___.

12. The day that follows Tuesday is ___.

13. They got lost, and we found ___.

14. More excellent than another is ___.

15. It didn't happen now, but ___.

16. The mystery word comes from the Latin word *centum*. *Centum* means hundred. Other words also come from *centum*. One hundred years is called a century. A bug with one hundred legs is called a centipede. In Mexico, one hundred centavos make a peso. In America, one hundred ___ make a dollar. Can you guess the mystery word? ___

37

Lily

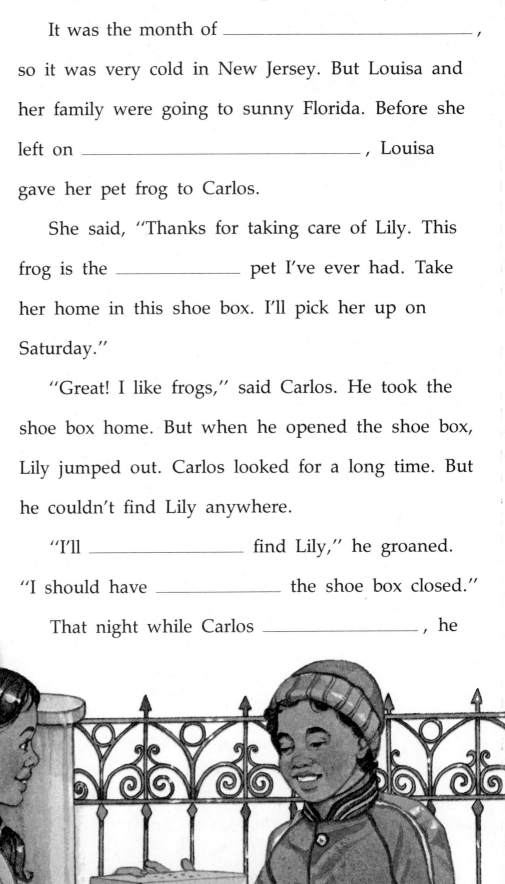

Use each word once to complete this story.

It was the month of _____,
so it was very cold in New Jersey. But Louisa and
her family were going to sunny Florida. Before she
left on _____, Louisa
gave her pet frog to Carlos.

She said, "Thanks for taking care of Lily. This
frog is the _____ pet I've ever had. Take
her home in this shoe box. I'll pick her up on
Saturday."

"Great! I like frogs," said Carlos. He took the
shoe box home. But when he opened the shoe box,
Lily jumped out. Carlos looked for a long time. But
he couldn't find Lily anywhere.

"I'll _____ find Lily," he groaned.
"I should have _____ the shoe box closed."

That night while Carlos _____, he

dreamed about Lily. The next day Carlos told his

_____ , Roland, what had happened.

"Louisa is coming back in two days. I have to find

Lily by _____ ."

Roland said, "I have a _____

idea. Let's go to the pet store and buy another frog.

Louisa will never _____ it's not Lily."

There were _____ frogs at the pet store.

Carlos and Roland looked at _____ all.

They found one that looked just like Lily.

"Five dollars," said the saleswoman.

"We have only sixty _____ ," said

Carlos sadly. The saleswoman _____ the

boys away.

Saturday morning, Louisa came to get Lily.

Carlos opened the door. He didn't know what to

say. Suddenly Carlos heard a CROAK! Lily jumped

out of his jacket pocket.

"Lily!" said Louisa happily. "Thanks for taking

such good care of her, Carlos. And _____

we go away in _____ ,

maybe you'll take care of Lily again."

Carlos smiled. He'd tell Louisa tomorrow.

best
better
cents
February
never
kept
sent
September
slept
them
then
Wednesday
when
friend
many
guess

Capitals

Use a capital letter to begin the names of people and pets and for the word <u>I</u>.

> *<u>Adam</u> and <u>I</u> read a book about a dog named <u>Dominic</u>.*
> *A raccoon named <u>Macaroon</u> is in a book by <u>Julia</u> <u>Cunningham</u>.*

★ In the sentences below, find each word that should begin with a capital letter. Then write the sentence correctly. Draw a circle around any spelling words in your sentences.

1. c.w. anderson wrote books about a horse named blaze.

2. blaze was kept by a boy named billy.

3. a horse named thunderbolt became friends with billy and blaze.

4. <u>old yeller</u> is the book i like best.

5. old yeller belonged to travis.

6. faithful is the word for old yeller.

★ Think of stories you have read.

7. Write the names of animals from these stories.

LESSON 7

AFTER THE TEST...

1. Did you spell all the words on your test correctly? _____
   If you did, go on to WRITE NOW! If you missed a word, it is important to know why.

2. Did you forget to capitalize the first letter of <u>February</u>, <u>September</u>, or <u>Wednesday</u>? _____

3. Did you put letters in the wrong order in <u>friend</u> or <u>guess</u>?

   _____

4. Did you write <u>cent</u> instead of <u>sent</u>? _____

5. If you made some other mistake, what was it? _____

6. Write the words you missed.

   _____

   _____

NOW WHAT?

It helps some people to hear a word spelled out loud. If you have trouble with some spelling words, it may be fun to try this.

Start spelling the word as you bend to touch your toes. Touch your toes every time you spell a word. Do this faster and faster until you can spell all the words.

WRITE NOW!

Here are four more words with /ĕ/:
   leg present led anyone
Use two of these words to write a letter to a pen pal. Tell your pen pal about a gift that you didn't want.

41

Lesson 8   Words with /ē/

Listen for /ē/ as you say each word.

meet

need

sleep

street

queen

wheel

free

sneeze

dream

each

meat

read

sea

team

please

people

1. Write the word that begins with a vowel.

_____

2. Write two words that sound alike but are not spelled the same.

_____

3. Write two words that end with the last three letters of <u>cream</u>.

_____

4. Write two words that end with /z/.

_____

5. Which two words end with two vowel letters?

_____

6. Write the word that begins with the letters <u>qu</u>.

_____

7. Write two words that end with the letter <u>d</u>.

_____

8. Which word begins with the letters <u>st</u>?

_____

9. Write two words that end with /l/.

_____

10. Which word ends with the letter <u>p</u>?

_____

Checkpoint

Write a spelling word for each clue.
Then use the Checkpoint Study Plan on page 224.

1. If you don't have to pay, it's ____.

2. Human beings are ____.

3. A plane is to fly, a book is to ____.

4. Something to eat is ____.

5. When you have a cold, you might ____.

6. When you ask for something, say ____.

7. "Every single one" means ____.

8. Nine baseball players make a ____.

9. When you must have something, you ____ it .

10. Another word for ocean is ____.

11. When you are tired, you go to ____.

12. To come face to face is to ____.

13. Something that rolls is a ____.

14. A nightmare is a bad ____.

15. A road is a ____.

16. Sometimes the meaning of a word changes. This mystery word comes from the Old English word *cwen*. Long ago in England, *cwen* meant wife. Later it was used for only one special wife. She was the wife or *cwen* of the king. Guess the mystery word. Then you'll know what we say today instead of *cwen*. ____

43

Use each word once to complete this story.

Queen of the Roads

Many years ago, in a castle by the _____,
there lived a beautiful _____. She was a
good queen. The _____ in her
kingdom loved her. Her life was easy. But she was
unhappy because _____ day was just like
the day before. Each morning she would sit and
_____ the news of the day. Each afternoon
she would _____ with her advisers. Every
night she had a dinner of roasted _____,
hot cider, and sweet fruits.

But this did not _____ her.
Every night when she went to _____
she would _____ of leaving the castle.
"I _____ a change," the queen thought.

One day she told a servant, "Today I want to be
_____. Get a _____ of horses and
a carriage ready for me."

The queen got in the carriage. She rode alone.
She drove down the main _____.
All the people saw her and cheered.

44

"This will never do," she said. So she headed for the country. Suddenly, the carriage hit a big rock. A _____ flew off. The carriage was very heavy. The queen could not fix the wheel alone. It was getting dark and cold. She began to shake and _____ .

At last, two farmers came by. They helped the queen fix the wheel.

"Will you please give us a favor in return?" one farmer asked the queen.

"Anything you wish," the happy queen said.

"Build a new road so other carriages won't hit the rocks."

"It will be done," answered the queen. "I shall build new roads all over my kingdom!"

And the queen was so busy keeping her promise that she was never unhappy again.

meet
need
sleep
street
queen
wheel
free
sneeze
dream
each
meat
read
sea
team
please
people

Nouns

A noun is a word that names a person, place, thing, or idea.

boy   city   toy   beauty
girl   town   dog   peace

★ Write the noun in each group of words below.

1. walked   meat   up   2. queen   over   helping

3. ran   into   street   4. people   like   about

5. read   sea   swam   6. until   team   each

★ Decide which noun fits each unfinished sentence. Then write the sentence.

sneeze   wheel   sea   dream   people   street

7. I had a wonderful ___ last night.

8. All the ___ who live on my ___ were in it.

9. We sailed out to ___ in a big ship.

10. My little sister steered the ___ of the ship.

11. I woke up from my dream when I heard a loud ___!

Wrap Up

LESSON 8

AFTER THE TEST . . .

1. Did you spell all the words on your test correctly? _____

If you did, go on to WRITE NOW! If you missed a word, it is important to know why.

2. Did you write <u>see</u> instead of <u>sea</u>? _____

3. Did you leave a letter out of <u>people</u>? _____

4. Did you put letters in the wrong order in <u>please</u> or <u>dream</u>?

_____

5. If you made some other mistake, what was it? _____

6. Write the words you missed.

_____

_____

NOW WHAT ?

It helps some people to see a word written in a special way. If you have trouble with some words, it may be fun for you to try this.

Write your word in big letters on a piece of paper. Trace each letter with your finger. Say each letter as you trace it. Do this until you spell the word without looking.

WRITE NOW!

Here are four more words with /ē/:

feel leave real speed

Use two of these words to write a sports story. You might begin: Johnny Jones spent a year getting ready for the big race.

Lesson 9 Words with /ē/

Listen for /ē/ as you say each word.

happy

funny

very

busy

sleepy

carry

sunny

every

family

penny

only

city

story

these

even

key

1. Which three words begin with a vowel?

_____

_____

2. Which two words begin with /k/?

_____

3. Write the two words in which you hear /z/ but do not see the letter z.

_____

4. Write five words that have double consonants.

nn _____   nn _____

nn _____   pp _____

rr _____

5. Write the word in which you hear /ē/ in both syllables. _____

6. Which two words end with the letters ery?

_____

7. Which two words begin with the letter f?

_____

8. Which word ends with the last three letters of glory? _____

9. Write the word in which you hear /s/ but do not see the letter s. _____

Checkpoint

Write a spelling word for each clue.
Then use the Checkpoint Study Plan on page 224.

1. If it's just one, it's the one and ___.

2. If you can't pick it up, it's too heavy to ___.

3. A fairy tale is a kind of ___.

4. "Smooth, not rough" means ___.

5. A clown tries to make you laugh by being ___.

6. If you feel like taking a nap, you're ___.

7. If you have a lot of work to do, you're ___.

8. The opposite of sad is ___.

9. "Each one" means ___.

10. You open a lock with a ___.

11. A room that is full of sunlight is ___.

12. It's not those, but ___.

13. The test was ___ hard.

14. One cent is a ___.

15. A large town is a ___.

16. Long ago in Rome, rich people had many servants. Men servants were called *famuli*. Women servants were called *famulae*. Together they were called *familia*. Later, a husband, a wife, their children, and their servants were called a *familia*. Can you guess the mystery word that comes from *familia*? ___

49

Use each word once to complete these pages.

The Whole Tooth and Nothing But....

It all began on a bright, _____ day.

My brother Johnny is _____ six years old.

He dared me to pull out my loose tooth. He said

he would _____ my books to school for

a week if I did. I love my family very much. I

_____ love Johnny. But I don't let anyone

in my _____ call me a coward.

So I tied one end of a string around my dog

Red's collar. Red didn't look very _____

about it. In fact, he was _____, so I

had to wake him up. I was ready to tie the other

end around my tooth. Just then Fishstick, our cat,

ran in front of us. And Red ran after her.

The string got caught on my finger. And I was pulled along after Red. People stopped to laugh at us. We must have looked pretty _____.

Then Fishstick jumped up on an apple cart. Red jumped, too. When Red landed on the cart, _____ apple rolled into the street.

Just then, a masked man ran out of the bank. He was too _____ running to notice _____ apples. He went slipping and sliding. Before we knew it, the police had him.

Then I noticed that my tooth was missing. And I didn't even know where it had gone.

The next day, I read this _____ in the newspaper:

TROUBLE AT PENNY BANK

Friday began as a quiet day in the _____. Then a small girl, a big dog, and a cat turned over an apple cart in front of the _____ Bank. This was the _____ in the capture of Mr. X.

When asked how it felt to be a hero, Cissy Thomas said, "It's _____ nice. But has anyone found a missing tooth?"

happy
funny
very
busy
sleepy
carry
sunny
every
family
penny
only
city
story
these
even
key

51

Alphabetical Order

The words in a dictionary are in alphabetical order.

★ Look at the Spelling Dictionary at the back of this book. Then complete these sentences.

1. Words that begin with **A** start on page _____ and end on page _____.

2. Words that begin with **K** start on page _____ and end on page _____.

3. Words that begin with **S** start on page _____ and end on page _____.

★ Write the words below in alphabetical order. Then find each one in the Spelling Dictionary and write the number of the page it is on.

funny   even   carry   key

	Words	Page		Words	Page
4.			5.		
6.			7.		

★ Write this story. Use these words in alphabetical order for the missing words in the story. You will need to capitalize one word.

very   story   only   city   busy   family   happy   penny   these

Cindy had a _____ Saturday. She went to the _____ with her

_____. The city always made her _____. But there was _____ so much

she could do in a day. Her mom took her to the _____ arcade.

They also went to a children's theater to hear a _____.

_____ were the two things she liked best in the city. Was she tired

when she got home? Yes, _____!

Wrap Up

LESSON 9

AFTER THE TEST . . .

1. Did you spell all the words on your test correctly? _____

   If you did, go on to WRITE NOW! If you missed a word, it is important to know why.

2. Did you put an <u>s</u> instead of a <u>c</u> at the beginning of <u>city</u>?

   _____

3. Did you put an extra letter in a word? _____

4. Did you leave a letter out of <u>family</u>? _____

5. If you made some other mistake, what was it? _____

6. Write the words you missed.

   _____

   _____

NOW WHAT ?

It helps some people to hear a word spelled out loud with rhythm. If you have trouble with some spelling words, it may be fun for you to try this.

Spell the word out loud. Clap your hands in between each letter. Do this until you can spell the word. You might have quite a beat when you have finished.

WRITE NOW!

Here are four more words with /ē/:
   lazy hurry easy evening
Use these words to tell what happened when you took a shortcut home from school. You might begin: It was late, so I . . .

Lesson 10 Words with /ŭ/

Listen for /ŭ/ as you say each word.

mother

front

month

money

from

other

nothing

Monday

such

summer

much

lunch

sun

under

Sunday

does

1. Which two words are always spelled with a capital letter?

   _____

2. In which word do you hear /z/ but see the letter s? _____

3. Which four words end with the letters er?

   _____

   _____

4. Write two words that begin with the letters fr.

   _____

5. Which three words begin with the first three letters of monkey? _____

   _____

6. Which word ends with the letters ing?

   _____

7. Write three words that end with the letters ch.

   _____

   _____

8. Which word sounds exactly like the word son but is not spelled the same way?

Checkpoint

Write a spelling word for each clue.
Then use the Checkpoint Study Plan on page 224.

1. The opposite of back is ____.

2. If you're not going to, you're coming ____.

3. He is ____ a good friend.

4. The night has the moon, and the day has the ____.

5. Something you put in the bank is ____.

6. The best time of year to go to the beach is ____.

7. The day that follows Sunday is ____.

8. The opposite of everything is ____.

9. October is the name of a ____.

10. He is my father, she is my ____.

11. I do, you do, and she ____.

12. It's not over, but ____.

13. The day after Saturday is ____.

14. It's not this one, but the ____.

15. "A lot" means the same as ____.

16. You probably use this mystery word every day. It comes from the Spanish word *longa*. *Longa* means piece. The mystery word also was used to mean piece in English. It was usually used to mean a piece of meat. People often ate a piece of meat at noon. So the noon meal took its name from this word. What is the word? ____

Use each word once to complete this story.

Face the Music

It was June, the last _____ of school. And this was the last weekend before _____ vacation. Josh's favorite day was Sunday. But not this _____ .

Yesterday Josh had found two dollars in his jacket. He could not remember where the money came _____ . But he knew how _____ he wanted a record. So he bought the record with the _____ .

Today he remembered! The two dollars was class money. The _____ kids had given him the money to buy Mr. Farar, the music teacher, a class present.

Josh didn't have any more money. And the record had been on sale. He couldn't return it. What could he do?

Josh was sad. His _____ asked what was wrong. He was so ashamed, he said, "It's _____ ."

Then Patty called. "How _____ Mr. Farar's present look?"

56

"Well . . ." Josh began.

"Remember to put a note on it. Don't forget all of our names."

Josh hung up the telephone. But Patty's words had given him a great idea. He found his clay _____ his bed. He formed the clay into an egg shape and stuck a stick into it. Josh dried it in the _____. Later he painted it silver.

_____ morning it was dry. He wrapped it and took it to school.

At noon he went to _____. Patty asked, "Where's the present and the note?"

"You'll see," said Josh.

Mr. Farar opened his gift in _____ of the class. "A record album and a silver music note with your names on it!" he exclaimed. "This took _____ a lot of work. This is one note I'll hold forever!"

mother
front
month
money
from
other
nothing
Monday
such
summer
much
lunch
sun
under
Sunday
does

Question Marks

Use a question mark (?) at the end of a sentence that asks a question.

Does Carlo like riddles?
Can he answer these?

★ Help Carlo answer these riddles. Copy each riddle. Be sure to add a question mark or a period. Then choose an answer.

Answers

a sponge   her lap   your teeth   the letter m

1. What comes once in a month, twice in a moment, and never in a hundred years _____

_____

Answer: _____

2. What does your friend lose whenever she stands up _____

_____

_____

Answer: _____

3. What is full of holes and still holds water _____

_____

Answer: _____

4. What can you put into the apple pie you have for lunch _____

_____

Answer: _____

AFTER THE TEST...

1. Did you spell all the words on your test correctly? _____
If you did, go on to WRITE NOW! If you missed a word, it is important to know why.

2. Did you leave a letter out of <u>does</u>? _____

3. Did you forget to double the letter <u>m</u> in <u>summer</u>? _____

4. Did you forget to capitalize the first letter of <u>Sunday</u> or <u>Monday</u>? _____

5. If you made some other mistake, what was it? _____

6. Write the words you missed.

_____

_____

_____

NOW WHAT ?

It helps some people to see a word written in color. If you have trouble with some spelling words, it may be fun for you to try this.

Write the word with a green crayon. Look at the word. Close your eyes. Can you see the word? Can you spell it? Do this until you can spell all the words.

WRITE NOW!

Here are four more words with /ŭ/:
truck son jump oven

Use two of the words in a story about a truck that can fly.

Lesson 11 Contractions

Say each word.

they'll
she'll
I'll
we'll
you'll

I've
we've
you've
they've

he's
she's
it's

I'd
you'd
they'd

I'm

1. Write the word that sounds exactly like <u>weave</u>.

_____

2. Write the word that sounds exactly like <u>its</u>.

_____

3. Write the word that sounds exactly like <u>aisle</u>.

_____

4. Which three words have the <u>ey</u> spelling of /ā/?

_____ _____

_____

5. Which five words have the <u>e</u> spelling of /ē/?

_____ _____

_____ _____

_____

6. Write the four words that always begin with a capital letter.

_____ _____

_____ _____

7. Write the three words that begin with the letter <u>y</u>.

_____ _____

_____

Checkpoint

Write a spelling word for each clue.
Then use the Checkpoint Study Plan on page 224.

1. she + will = ___

2. we + will = ___

3. I + will = ___

4. you + will = ___

5. they + will = ___

6. I + have = ___

7. they + have = ___

8. we + have = ___

9. you + have = ___

10. she + is = ___

11. it + is = ___

12. he + is = ___

13. they + would = ___

14. you + would = ___

15. I + am = ___

16. Verbs have different forms for past, present, and future action. Long ago, English verbs used to have even more forms. A few of these forms are still used today. The mystery word is a special form of the verb <u>will</u>. It used to be spelled *wolde*. Guess how we spell *wolde* today. Then make a contraction with the word <u>I</u> to get the mystery word. ___

Use each word once to complete this story.

DIARY OF A DETECTIVE - CASE #13

I went over to Pete's house for dinner. The first thing he said was, "We are having roast beef. _____ defrosting in the kitchen right now."

I know Pete. And _____ always hungry. I'm not. _____ rather work on a mystery than eat.

We were in the yard. Then we heard a loud bang inside the house. "_____ sure it's not Mom. _____ still at work. _____ be home in an hour."

We ran to the house. The back door was wide open. In the kitchen, a chair was on its side. In the hall, my coat was on the floor. We heard a strange noise upstairs. "Let's go next door and call the police," whispered Pete. "_____ know what to do. _____ handled lots of burglars."

I didn't think it was burglars because _____ be very quiet. Then I noticed something. "_____ got it!" I yelled.

"Ssh!" said Pete. "If you are not quiet,

_____ scare them off!"

"Together _____ be able to handle this,"
I said. "_____ got all the clues we need.
Look around."

Pete looked. Then he said, "The beef is missing!
What kind of burglar would take a piece of meat?
And look at the floor. Where did those paw prints
come from?"

Before I could answer, a puppy came down the
steps. He barked at us.

Pete laughed. He said, "Well, puppy. I see that

_____ eaten our dinner. Now I suppose

_____ like some dessert."

The dog just wagged his tail. He trotted out the
door. But _____ bet he was happy.

they'll
she'll
I'll
we'll
you'll
I've
we've
you've
they've
he's
she's
it's
I'd
you'd
they'd
I'm

Apostrophes

A contraction is one word made from two words. It is easier and quicker to say than the two words. A contraction has at least one letter and sound left out. An apostrophe (') shows where those letters have been left out.

Two Words	Contraction	Left Out
I am	*I'm*	*a*
we have	*we've*	*ha*

★ Write the contraction for each set of words. Then write the letters that you left out.

Two Words	Contraction	Left Out
1. they will		
2. she has		
3. it is		
4. she will		
5. he is		
6. you have		
7. I have		

★ Choose four contractions and use each one in a sentence.

8. _____

9. _____

10. _____

11. _____

Wrap Up

★ ★ ★

LESSON 11

AFTER THE TEST . . .

1. Did you spell all the words on your test correctly? _____

   If you did, go on to WRITE NOW! If you missed a word, it is important to know why.

2. Did you leave out an apostrophe (')? _____

3. Did you forget to capitalize the word I? _____

4. Did you write will instead of we'll? _____

5. If you made some other mistake, what was it? _____

6. Write the words you missed.

   _____

   _____

NOW WHAT ?

It helps some people to see a word in color. If you have trouble with some spelling words, it may be fun to try this.

Write each contraction you missed on a separate card. Write it in red. Stare at the contraction. Then turn the card over and spell the word without looking.

WRITE NOW!

Here are four more contractions:
he'd she'd he'll we'd
Use two of these words to write

what two friends said to each other about the new school crossing guard.

Lesson 12 Words in Review

A. slept

friend

many

guess

B. meet

queen

team

please

people

C. family

these

even

key

D. month

such

does

★Use a piece of paper for the starred activities.

1. In Lesson 7 you studied four ways to spell /ĕ/: **e, ie, a, ue.** Write the words in list A.

_____ _____

_____ _____

2. In Lesson 8 you studied three ways to spell /ē/: **ee, ea, eo.** Write the words in list B.

_____ _____

_____ _____

★**3.** Now write a sentence for each review word in lists A and B.

4. In Lesson 9 you studied three more ways to spell /ē/: **y, e, ey.** Write the words in list C.

_____ _____

_____ _____

5. In Lesson 10 you studied three ways to spell /ŭ/: **o, u, oe.** Write the words in list D.

_____ _____

_____ _____

★**6.** Write the review words in lists C and D. Look up each word in the Spelling Dictionary and write the sound spelling next to each word.

★**7.** Now, put all the words in lists A and B in alphabetical order.

Proof It Yourself

The sentences below have been proofread. The proofreading marks tell you what mistakes have to be corrected.

- _sp_ means that the word is misspelled.
- ≡ means that a letter should be a capital.

I read a (storie) about a lion named elsa.

I read a story about a lion named Elsa.

Write the sentences correctly. Use each sentence to begin a paragraph. Write each paragraph on another paper. Proofread your work.

1. I (ges) that (Im) going to camp this july.

_____

_____

2. Today mrs. logan said to me, "Come here, (pleez)."

_____

_____

3. maggie barks at (evrie) dog she sees, except Bruno.

_____

_____

4. On friday afternoons, my class (duz) something I love to do.

_____

_____

5. i hope (youl) like riding the camel as much as I did.

_____

_____

Lesson 13 Words with /ŭ/

Listen for /ŭ/ as you say each word.

won

lovely

done

one

shove

some

something

cover

hundred

must

butter

supper

number

just

sum

1. Write four words that end with the letters <u>er</u>.

_____

_____

2. Which word is made up of two words put together? _____

3. Write two words beginning with the letter <u>s</u> that sound exactly alike but are not spelled alike.

_____

4. Write two other words that sound exactly alike but are spelled differently.

_____

5. Which two words end with the letters <u>st</u>?

_____

6. In which three words do you hear /v/?

_____

_____

7. Write three words that have the letters <u>one</u>.

_____

_____

8. Write the word that begins with the first three letters of <u>hunt</u>. _____

9. Write two words that have double consonants.

pp _____   tt _____

Checkpoint

Write a spelling word for each clue.
Then use the Checkpoint Study Plan on page 224.

1. "Push" means ___.

2. The opposite of all is ___.

3. Ten is a ___.

4. Another word for pretty is ___.

5. If you are completely finished, you're ___.

6. When you add numbers, the answer is the ___.

7. The opposite of nothing is ___.

8. The last meal of the day is ___.

9. Three minus two leaves ___.

10. If you have to, you ___.

11. One team lost, the other team ___.

12. The number after 99 is one ___.

13. More than none, but not all is ___.

14. The opposite of unjust is ___.

15. Another word for lid is ___.

16. This mystery word comes from the Greek word
    bousturos. *Bous* meant cow. *Turos* meant
    cheese. The Romans learned this word from
    the Greeks. But they changed the word to
    butyrum. Write the mystery word. ___

69

The First Horse Show

Stacey rubbed her eyes and looked out her bedroom window. "What a _____ day for my first horse show," she thought.

"Stacey, you _____ get up now. We will be late for the show," her father called.

Stacey began to feel funny. It felt like there was _____ caught in her throat. And _____ then she heard her father walking toward her room. She threw the _____ over her head.

"Stacey, why aren't you up yet?" her father called to her.

"I don't think I can make it," she cried.

"Sure you can," he said. He gave her a gentle _____. "Everyone is scared before a show. Even after a _____ shows, you'll still feel this way."

Dad could always get Stacey going. She quickly dressed and grabbed a piece of warm toast with _____. She knew she would be sorry later if she didn't eat.

70

Ryan watched his sister eat. "May I have _____ more toast?" he asked. Ryan was always hungry. He knew it would be a long time until lunch and _____.

Soon they arrived at the arena. Stacey signed in. She would be _____ ten. "A great number," she thought. "It's the _____ of nine, my age, and _____ for first place."

Stacey got on her pony, Sunshine. She entered the big riding ring. As she finished the jumping course, Stacey hoped that _____ of the others had _____ as well as she had.

Stacey was still holding her breath when she heard the judge say, "In first place, Stacey riding Sunshine."

"We won!" she whispered to Sunshine. "We really _____."

won
lovely
done
one
shove
some
something
cover
none
hundred
must
butter
supper
number
just
sum

Homophones

Words that sound alike but are spelled differently and have different meanings are called <u>homophones</u>. The following words are homophones. Do you know what each word means?

<u>one</u> and <u>won</u>
<u>some</u> and <u>sum</u>

★ Rewrite each sentence using a correct homophone from above in each blank. Use the Spelling Dictionary to find meanings.

1. Jack ___ two blue ribbons and ___ trophy.

_____

2. Jill found the ___ of ___ numbers.

_____

★ Use these homophones to write the following sentences.

ate	**son**
eight	**sun**

3. Jason ___ his supper. _____

_____

4. The ___ looked lovely after the rain. _____

_____

5. We just met her daughter and her ___. _____

_____

6. My favorite number is ___. _____

_____

Wrap Up

LESSON 13

AFTER THE TEST...

1. Did you spell all the words on your test correctly? _____

   If you did, go on to WRITE NOW! If you missed a word, it is important to know why.

2. Did you forget the <u>d</u> in the middle of <u>hundred</u>? _____

3. Did you forget the letter <u>e</u> at the end of a word? _____

4. Did you write <u>one</u> instead of <u>won</u>? _____

5. Write the words you missed.

   _____

   _____

WRITE NOW!

Here are four more words with /ŭ/:

everyone someone color once

Use three of these words to write a story about a prince and a princess who had a contest to see who would rule the land.

NOW WHAT ?

It helps some people to hear a word spelled out loud. If you have trouble with some spelling words, it may be fun to try this.

Look at a word you missed while someone says it correctly. Close your eyes and try to see the word. With your eyes still closed, say and spell the word out loud.

Open your eyes and write the word. Did you spell it correctly? Say it again while you look at it. Do this until you can spell it.

Lesson 14 Words with /ĭ/

Listen for /ĭ/ as you say each word.

think

winter

children

dish

fill

little

thing

spring

kick

river

which

pretty

December

begin

build

been

1. Which three words end with the letters <u>er</u>?

_____ _____

2. Which three words have double consonants?

ll _____ tt _____

tt _____

3. Write the word in which the letters <u>ee</u> spell /ĭ/.

_____

4. Which word ends with the letters <u>sh</u>?

_____

5. Write two words that have the letters <u>ch</u>.

_____ _____

6. Which two words end with /k/?

_____ _____

7. Which two words end with the letters <u>ng</u>?

_____ _____

8. In which word do the letters <u>ui</u> spell /ĭ/?

_____

9. Which word begins with the letter <u>b</u> and has

two syllables? _____

10. Which word is always spelled with a capital

letter? _____

Checkpoint

Write a spelling word for each clue.
Then use the Checkpoint Study Plan on page 224.

1. The opposite of big is ____.

2. Another word for start is ____.

3. The opposite of ugly is ____.

4. You can swim in a brook, a stream, or a ____.

5. Yesterday you built, today you ____.

6. "What one" means the same as ____.

7. The season that follows winter is ____.

8. A noun names a person, a place, or a ____.

9. The coldest season of the year is ____.

10. I am, I was, I have ____.

11. To make something full is to ____.

12. With your brain you ____.

13. You serve food in a ____.

14. Boys and girls are ____.

15. To hit with your foot is to ____.

16. The Romans divided the year into ten months. The last Roman month was named *decem*. *Decem* meant ten. Our word for the last month comes from this word. But since we have twelve months, not ten, the number is no longer right. The mystery word comes from *decem*. Can you guess it? ____

John and Apple Pie

The _____ of P.S. 103 wanted to plant trees. In the playground, Jessie and Evan talked about what kind of tree they wanted.

"I _____ we should plant a fir tree," said Evan. "It would stay green, even when it snows in _____." Evan kicked a ball to Jessie. They began to _____ the ball around the playground while they talked.

"Fir trees are _____," said Jessie. "But I think we should _____ with an apple tree, in honor of Johnny Appleseed."

"Who's Johnny Appleseed?" asked Evan.

"I've _____ reading about him," said Jessie. The children stopped playing. Jessie told Evan more. "His real name was John Chapman. He was born in Massachusetts. In 1800, he was in Pennsylvania and he crossed a big _____ to Ohio. He planted seeds along the way. Soon, _____ trees began to grow all over the countryside."

"Did he keep planting trees?" asked Evan.

"Yes. From January to _____ he planted them. He wanted to _____ America with apple orchards. He took loving care of the orchards _____ he planted. His trees blossomed every _____.

"Some people thought he was strange. He wore tattered clothing. Then he did a very special _____ that changed people's minds. During the War of 1812, he traveled many kilometers to warn American troops about an attack. Now what do you think about an apple tree?"

"You'll get my vote for an apple tree," said Evan.

"Did my story convince you?" asked Jessie.

"No," answered Evan. "I want an apple tree because apple pie is my favorite _____!"

Evan ran as Jessie threw the ball at him.

think
winter
children
dish
fill
little
thing
spring
kick
river
which
pretty
December
begin
been

Capitals

The names of streets always begin with a capital letter. When the words <u>road</u>, <u>street</u>, and <u>avenue</u> come after the street name, they must begin with a capital, too.

Pam Katz lives on <u>Wayside Street</u>.
What street do you live on?

★ Study the map. Then write the answers.

1. Maria's house is on ____.

2. The school is on ____.

3. Enter the post office parking lot from ____.

4. The three streets that border the park are ____, ____, and ____.

5. Enter the picnic area from ____.

6. The only café is called ____. It is on ____.

Wrap Up

LESSON 14

AFTER THE TEST...

1. Did you spell all the words on

   your test correctly? _____
   If you did, go on to WRITE NOW! If you missed a word, it is important to know why.

2. Did you forget to capitalize the

   first letter of <u>December</u>? _____

3. Did you put letters in the

   wrong order? _____

4. Did you forget the first <u>h</u> in

   <u>which</u>? _____

5. If you made some other mistake,

   what was it? _____

6. Write the words you missed.

   _____

   _____

   _____

NOW WHAT?

It helps some people to see and hear a word spelled. If you have trouble with some spelling words, it may be fun for you to try this.

Write each word. Make each letter bigger than the one before it. Then spell the word out loud. Say each letter louder than the one before it. Make each letter sound as big as it looks!

WRITE NOW!

Here are four more words with /ĭ/:
list everything lives still
Use two of these words to write a story about a strange shopping list. You might want to begin: Dad sent me to do the shopping.

Lesson 15 Words with /ī/

Listen for /ī/ as you say each word.

line

drive

inside

nice

shine

while

size

miles

write

mine

alike

times

white

tiny

lion

eyes

1. Write two words that begin and end with a vowel.

_____

2. Which three words begin with the letter <u>w</u>?

_____

_____

3. Write the word that ends with /ē/.

_____

4. Which word begins with /s/ and ends with /z/?

_____

5. Write four words that end with /n/.

_____

_____

6. Which three words end with the letter <u>s</u>?

_____

_____

7. Write the word in which you hear /s/ but do not see the letter <u>s</u>. _____

8. Write the word that begins with the first three letters of <u>dried</u>. _____

9. In which word do you see the letter <u>e</u> twice?

_____

Checkpoint

Write a spelling word for each clue.
Then use the Checkpoint Study Plan on page 224.

1. To make a car go is to ——.

2. "Very, very small" means ——.

3. "A little later" means in a little ——.

4. To measure long distances, we use ——.

5. "Not rude, but pleasant" means ——.

6. The sun and the stars ——.

7. You can use a ruler to draw a straight ——.

8. Something that belongs to me is ——.

9. A baby wears a small ——.

10. The opposite of outside is ——.

11. You use a pencil to ——.

12. You see with your ——.

13. Things that are the same are ——.

14. The color of snow is ——.

15. "Multiplied by" means ——.

16. This mystery word comes from the Greek word *lēon*. Many names come from this mystery word. Leona, Lenore, Leo, Leopold, and Lionel all come from it. The mystery word means a big, wild animal. Can you guess it? ——

Use each word once to complete this story.

Just a BIG Cat

The lion belongs to the cat family. You might even say that a _____ is just a big cat.

A wild lion and a house cat are very much _____. They both have claws that they can pull _____ their paws. This keeps their claws _____ and sharp. Lions and house cats have _____ that see well in the dark. If a light should _____ on their eyes at night, their eyes will glow.

But lions are very different from house cats. The greatest difference is _____. A male lion can weigh 500 pounds, _____ a house cat will weigh about 10 pounds. A house cat seems _____ next to a lion.

The lion's fur is brownish-yellow. This color makes it easy for the lion to hide. A house cat can be many colors. It can even be snowy _____.

A male lion is the only cat that has a mane. The mane makes him look bigger and stronger.

Lions live in groups called prides. At _____, as many as 35 lions may live in a pride. These lions will hunt together. They usually walk about five _____ a day.

Lions don't let other animals hunt on their land. They roar as if to say, "Keep out! This land is _____." That may be why the lion is called "King of the Beasts."

Today, most lions live in Africa. But lions can be seen in parks and zoos. People _____ from far away and stand in a long _____ to see a lion.

Many people _____ books about lions. Even though people are afraid of lions, most still think lions are beautiful animals.

83

line
drive
inside
nice
shine
while
size
miles
write
mine
alike
times
white
tiny
lion
eyes

Guide Words

The two words in dark letters at the top of each dictionary page are called <u>guide words</u>. All the words on a dictionary page are arranged between the two guide words. The guide word at the left is the first word on the page. The other guide word is the last entry word on the page.

★Look at this Spelling Dictionary page.

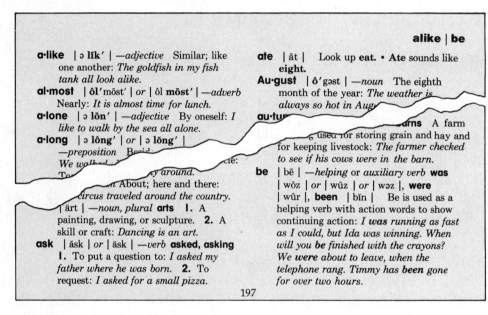

alike | be

a·like | ə līk′ | —*adjective* Similar; like one another: *The goldfish in my fish tank all look alike.*

al·most | ôl′mōst′ | *or* | ôl mōst′ | —*adverb* Nearly: *It is almost time for lunch.*

a·lone | ə lōn′ | —*adjective* By oneself: *I like to walk by the sea all alone.*

a·long | ə lông′ | *or* | ə lŏng′ | —*preposition* Besid... *We walked ...* ...cle: *To ... ...y around.* ... About; here and there: *circus traveled around the country.* | ärt | —*noun, plural* **arts** I. A painting, drawing, or sculpture. 2. A skill or craft: *Dancing is an art.*

ask | ăsk | *or* | äsk | —*verb* **asked, asking** I. To put a question to: *I asked my father where he was born.* 2. To request: *I asked for a small pizza.*

ate | āt | Look up **eat.** • Ate sounds like **eight.**

Au·gust | ô′gəst | —*noun* The eighth month of the year: *The weather is always so hot in Aug...*

au·tu... ...arns A farm ...used for storing grain and hay and for keeping livestock: *The farmer checked to see if his cows were in the barn.*

be | bē | —*helping* or *auxiliary verb* **was** | wŏz | *or* | wŭz | *or* | wəz |, **were** | wûr |, **been** | bĭn | Be is used as a helping verb with action words to show continuing action: *I was running as fast as I could, but Ida was winning. When will you be finished with the crayons? We were about to leave, when the telephone rang. Timmy has been gone for over two hours.*

197

1. What are the guide words? _____

   and _____

2. What is the first entry word? _____

3. What is the last entry word? _____

★Look up these spelling words in the dictionary at the back of the book. Write the guide words and page number for each.

<u>Guide Words</u>   Page

4. while _____

5. drive _____

6. nice _____

Wrap Up

LESSON 15

AFTER THE TEST . . .

1. Did you spell all the words on your test correctly? _____

   If you did, go on to WRITE NOW! If you missed a word, it is important to know why.

2. Did you leave out a letter?

   _____

3. Did you forget the letter <u>h</u> in <u>while</u>? _____

4. Did you forget the letter <u>e</u> at the end of a word? _____

5. If you made some other mistake, what was it? _____

6. Write the words you missed.

   _____

   _____

   _____

NOW WHAT ?

It helps some people to do something as they spell a word out loud. If you have trouble with some spelling words, it may be fun for you to try this.

Stand up and spell each word out loud. Jump every time you say a vowel. Do this until you can spell all the words.

WRITE NOW!

Here are four more words with /ī/:

dime   wide   sides   smile

Invent a toothpaste that comes in every color of the rainbow. Use two of these words in an advertisement.

Lesson 16 Words with /ī/

Listen for /ī/ as you say each word.

Friday

kind

child

mind

behind

high

right

light

night

by

cry

sky

try

why

fly

buy

1. Which two words have two syllables?

_____ _____

2. Which two words sound exactly the same but are not spelled the same?

_____ _____

3. Which three words have the last four letters of <u>sight</u>? _____

_____ _____

4. Write the word that begins and ends with the letter <u>h</u>. _____

5. Write three words that end with the last three letters of <u>find</u>. _____

_____ _____

6. Write six words that spell /ī/ with the letter <u>y</u>.

_____ _____

_____ _____

7. Which word begins with the letters <u>ch</u>?

_____

8. Which word always begins with a capital letter?

_____

Checkpoint

Write a spelling word for each clue.
Then use the Checkpoint Study Plan on page 224.

1. The opposite of mean is ___.

2. The time between sunset and sunrise is ___.

3. Tears come out of your eyes when you ___.

4. To pay money for something is to ___.

5. If you follow someone, you are ___.

6. The last day of school each week is ___.

7. The part of you that thinks is your ___.

8. Rabbits hop, and birds ___.

9. The opposite of low is ___.

10. "To make an effort" means to ___.

11. You ask what, when, where, and ___.

12. "Beside" or "near to" means ___.

13. The sun gives us heat and ___.

14. The opposite of left is ___.

15. A boy or a girl is a ___.

16. This mystery word comes from the Old English word *skie*. *Skie* meant cloud. *Skie* also meant the place where you see clouds. That's what the word means today. Guess the word. ___

Living Room Circus

Last _____ my family and I were going to the circus. But I got sick.

Mom made a bed for me on the couch. Then she opened the door to let Tinker in.

Tinker is our cat. He sleeps all day in the warm _____ of the sun. Every _____ he gets to play. I always _____ to talk Mom and Dad into letting me stay up all night. If a cat can, _____ can't I? They don't agree.

Well, that day, Tinker dropped a fat pigeon _____ my dad's feet.

"Oh, no," Mom cried. "How could you bring that in the house?"

Mom thinks you can talk to Tinker like you can talk to a _____. She gets very angry when Tinker acts like a cat. Mom doesn't allow that _____ of behavior from anyone!

Just then, the bird fluttered its wings. It wasn't dead. It began to _____ around the room. It flew _____ up to the ceiling.

Tinker saw the pigeon and hid _____ the couch. He jumped out as the bird whizzed by.

Mom opened the door. Tinker chased the pigeon. Dad chased Tinker. My baby brother began to _____. And I began to laugh. You couldn't _____ a ticket to a better show.

Finally, the bird flew out the door. Tinker was _____ behind it. But the pigeon flew high into the _____.

I was glad that the bird was safe. And I didn't _____ that I was sick. I got to see a circus after all!

89

Alphabetical Order

Many words begin with the same letter. To put these words in alphabetical order, look at the second letter of each word. Begin your list with the word in which the second letter comes first in the alphabet.

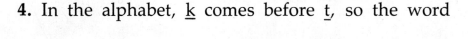 Look at the two words below.

s<u>k</u>y   s<u>t</u>ory

1. These words both start with the letter <u>s</u>. To put them in

   alphabetical order, look at the _____ letter.

2. The second letter in <u>sk</u>y is ____ .

3. The second letter in <u>st</u>ory is ____ .

4. In the alphabet, <u>k</u> comes before <u>t</u>, so the word

   _____ comes before the word _____ .

 In each list below, the words begin with the same letter. Look at the second letter of each word. Then write the words in alphabetical order.

5. **buy   behind   by**   6. **cry   child   cart**

   _____   _____

   _____   _____

   _____   _____

7. **fly   Friday   finish**   8. **light   late   llama**

   _____   _____

   _____   _____

Wrap Up ★★★

LESSON 16

AFTER THE TEST...

1. Did you spell all the words on your test correctly? _____
   If you did, go on to WRITE NOW! If you missed a word, it is important to know why.

2. Did you leave <u>gh</u> out of a word? _____

3. Did you write <u>by</u> instead of <u>buy</u>? _____

4. Did you forget to capitalize the first letter of <u>Friday</u>? _____

5. If you made some other mistake, what was it? _____

6. Write the words you missed.

   _____

   _____

   _____

NOW WHAT?

It helps some people to hear a word spelled in a special way. If you have trouble with some words, it may be fun for you to try this.

Say the word. Spell the word. Snap your fingers after each letter. Do this faster and faster until you can spell the word faster than you can snap your fingers.

WRITE NOW!

Here are four more words with /ī/:
wild fine quiet bright

Use three of these words to write a weather report.

Lesson 17 Adding ed and ing

Say each word.

wished

asked

dreamed

rained

handed

painted

filled

subtracted

thanked

waited

reading

sleeping

meeting

laughing

guessing

ending

Complete the word equations.

1. fill   +   ed   = _____

2. ask   +   ed   = _____

3. rain   +   ed   = _____

4. wait   +   ed   = _____

5. wish   +   ed   = _____

6. hand   +   ed   = _____

7. paint   +   ed   = _____

8. thank   +   ed   = _____

9. dream   +   ed   = _____

10. subtract   +   ed   = _____

11. end   +   ing   = _____

12. read   +   ing   = _____

13. meet   +   ing   = _____

14. sleep   +   ing   = _____

15. laugh   +   ing   = _____

16. guess   +   ing   = _____

Answer this question.

17. In which three words do the letters <u>ed</u> spell /t/?

_____

Checkpoint

Write a spelling word for each clue.
Then use the Checkpoint Study Plan on page 224.

1. The last part of a story is the ___.

2. Are you right-handed or left-___.

3. "Made a picture with paints" means ___.

4. If you made a wish, you ___.

5. "Went to sleep and had a dream" means ___.

6. The opposite of crying is ___.

7. When people get together to talk, it's a ___.

8. Giving an answer you're not sure about is ___.

9. "Stayed until someone came" means ___.

10. When you're not awake, you're ___.

11. "Put a question to someone" means ___.

12. If water fell from the sky, then it ___.

13. "Told someone thank you" means ___.

14. The opposite of emptied is ___.

15. Libraries have books for ___.

16. This mystery word means to take away or to make less. It comes from two Latin words. The words are *sub* and *trahere*. *Sub* meant below or away. *Trahere* meant to pull. *Subtrahere* meant to pull away. Can you guess the word made from *subtrahere* + <u>ed</u>? ___

Use each word once to complete this story.

THE PLAYOFFS

When I left hockey practice last night, it was still raining. It had _____ all day.

I _____ for my dad to pick me up. Then I remembered that Mom and Dad were at a _____ with my teachers. So I walked over to school to wait.

I tried not to think about the homework that I hadn't done yet. I had extra problems to do because I added numbers on our last test when I should have _____ them. Oh, how I _____ that I had done my math before practice. Then I would have been finished.

At school I ran into Ms. Ford, the art teacher. She was showing the parents pictures that students had _____ . Mr. Chan, the librarian, was also at school. I _____ if I could wait in the library. He said yes. Then he _____ me a book that he was sure I would like. I _____ him and sat at a table.

94

The book was about the hockey goalie, Gerry Cheevers. It was _____ with pictures. I started _____ . The book was great. I could hardly wait to read the _____ .

The next thing I knew, I was on the floor, swinging my arms and yelling. My parents were there. They were _____ at me. I shook my head and blinked. "Was I _____ ?" I asked.

"I'm only _____ ," Dad said, "but I would say you _____ you were a hockey player. The way you were swinging your arms around, I'm glad I wasn't the other guy!"

I grinned. Too bad it was just a dream.

95

Exclamation Points

Use an exclamation point (!) at the end of a sentence that shows strong feeling or surprise.

Open that door!
I'm so happy you're here!

★ Write each sentence below. Put an exclamation point, a period, or a question mark at the end of each sentence.

1. Betsy asked, "Who painted this picture "

2. She was guessing that Paul had done it

3. She found Paul sleeping

4. Betsy shouted, "Boo "

5. Paul jumped up fast

6. "Oh, Betsy " he yelled. "Now I'll never know the ending of my dream "

7. Then they both started laughing

Wrap Up

LESSON 17

AFTER THE TEST...

1. Did you spell all the words on your test correctly? _____
If you did, go on to WRITE NOW! If you missed a word, it is important to know why.

2. Did you double a letter when you shouldn't have? _____

3. Did you leave out a letter?

_____

4. Did you put letters in the wrong order in <u>guessing</u> or <u>laughing</u>? _____

5. If you made some other mistake, what was it? _____

6. Write the words you missed.

_____

NOW WHAT?

Some people learn best by writing a word. If you have trouble with some spelling words, it may be fun to try this.

Write the word you missed. Then trace over the <u>ed</u> or <u>ing</u> ending with a red crayon. Stare at the word. Can you still see the word? Close your eyes and spell it.

WRITE NOW!

Here are four more words with the <u>ed</u> ending:

looked needed headed helped

Use two of the words in a letter about losing an oar in the lake. You might begin:

Dear Pat,

Today I went rowing.

97

Lesson 18 Words in Review

A. won

lovely

hundred

B. kick

river

pretty

build

been

C. shine

tiny

lion

eyes

D. behind

high

sky

buy

★ Use a piece of paper for the starred activities.

1. In Lesson 13 you studied two ways to spell /ŭ/: **o, u.** Write the words in list A.

_____

_____

2. In Lesson 14 you studied four ways to spell /ĭ/: **i, e, ui, ee.** Write the words in list B.

_____

_____

★**3.** Now write the review words in lists A and B. Look them up in the Spelling Dictionary and write the sound spelling next to each word.

4. In Lesson 15 you studied three ways to spell /ī/: **i_e, i, eye.** Write the words in list C.

_____

_____

5. In Lesson 16 you studied three more ways to spell /ī/: **i, y, uy.** Write the words in list D.

_____

_____

★**6.** Now write a sentence for each review word in lists C and D.

★**7.** Write sentences for the words in A and B.

★**8.** Write the review words from lists C and D in alphabetical order.

Proof It Yourself

The sentences below have been proofread. The proofreading marks tell you what mistakes have to be corrected.

- *sp* means that the word is misspelled.
- = means that a letter should be a capital.

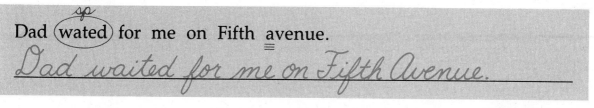

Dad (wated) for me on Fifth avenue.

Dad waited for me on Fifth Avenue.

Write the sentences correctly. Use each sentence to begin a paragraph. Write each paragraph on another paper. Proofread your work.

1. I wish i had one (hundrit) colors in my crayon box.

_____

_____

2. Now tina knows (witch) kitten she wants for a pet.

_____

_____

3. The family in the (wite) house on jay street must have pets.

_____

_____

4. (Buy) night, the (lite) rain had become a storm.

_____

_____

5. pam (wisht) she could sled down the blane avenue hill.

_____

_____

Lesson 19 Words with /ŏ/

Listen for /ŏ/ as you say each word.

sorry

socks

clock

bottom

block

problem

jog

o'clock

October

forgot

shop

bottle

body

wash

what

was

1. In which four words do the letters <u>ck</u> spell /k/?

_____ _____

_____ _____

2. Which three words have double consonants?

rr _____ tt _____

tt _____

3. Which two words have the letters <u>sh</u>?

_____ _____

4. Write two words that have only three letters.

_____ _____

5. In which word does the letter <u>s</u> spell /z/?

_____

6. Which word is always spelled with a capital letter? _____

7. Write a word that begins with /hw/.

_____

8. Write two words that end with the vowel /ē/.

_____

9. Which word begins with the letter <u>p</u> and has two syllables? _____

10. Which word begins with the letter <u>f</u> and has two syllables? _____

Checkpoint

Write a spelling word for each clue.
Then use the Checkpoint Study Plan on page 224.

1. When you buy food, you ____.

2. To clean with water and soap is to ____.

3. From your head to your feet is your ____.

4. To run slowly is to ____.

5. If you're sad you did something, you're ____.

6. Over your feet and under your shoes are ____.

7. From one street corner to another is one ____.

8. Today I am, yesterday I ____.

9. "Which thing" means ____.

10. The opposite of remembered is ____.

11. A container that holds liquids is a ____.

12. The month before November is ____.

13. A word for "of the clock" is ____.

14. The lowest part of anything is the ____.

15. A hard question to answer is a ____.

16. This mystery word names an instrument that tells the time of day. The word comes from the Old French word *cloque*. *Cloque* meant bell. These instruments used to be made with bells. The bells rang when a new hour arrived. Today only a few of these instruments have bells. Can you guess the mystery word? ____

The Problem with Penny

The _____ with Penny was that she read too many mystery books. In September she had read 15 mysteries. So far, in the month of _____ she had read 12. Marie _____ tired of hearing about Penny's mysteries. She decided to cure Penny.

That afternoon, when the _____ struck four, Penny went for her daily two-mile _____. She went around the _____ and into the center of town. Then she jogged by the candy _____ and headed down to the lake. As she ran by the lake, something caught her eye. It looked like a milk _____ floating in the lake. She could see something white at the _____ of the bottle. And it was not milk. She could hardly believe it. Here was her chance to solve a real mystery.

It was getting late. Penny had to be home by five _____. She was in such a hurry to get the bottle that she _____ to be careful. SPLASH! From her feet to her head

Penny's _____ was soaked. But she had the bottle. She wondered _____ the message would say. Quickly, Penny opened the bottle. She shook out the piece of paper. It said:

I am _____ you had to go through all this. I'll bet your shoes and _____ are soaking wet. I hope this will _____ away your taste for mysteries.

Guess who?

sorry
socks
clock
bottom
block
problem
jog
o'clock
October
forgot
shop
bottle
body
wash
what
was

Alphabetical Order

⭐ Look at these sample entry words from a dictionary:

block   bottle   butter

1. What is the same about the words? _____

Words that begin with the same letter are put into alphabetical order by using the second letter.

b<u>l</u>ock   b<u>o</u>ttle   b<u>u</u>tter

. . . k l m n o p q r s t u v . . .

⭐ Look at the second letter of each word. Then write each group of words in alphabetical order.

2. bottle block bank butter   **3.** shop salt socks stack

_____   _____

_____   _____

_____   _____

_____   _____

4. was wonder west what   **5.** problem paint plaster pound

_____   _____

_____   _____

_____   _____

6. October   orange   often   other

_____

_____

_____

_____

Wrap Up

LESSON 19

AFTER THE TEST...

1. Did you spell all the words on your test correctly? _____
If you did, go on to WRITE NOW! If you missed a word, it is important to know why.

2. Did you forget to capitalize the first letter of <u>October</u>? _____

3. Did you forget the apostrophe (') in <u>o'clock</u>? _____

4. Did you leave a letter out of <u>socks</u>? _____

5. If you made some other mistake, what was it? _____

6. Write the words you missed.

_____

_____

_____

NOW WHAT?

It helps some people to hear a word spelled in a special way. If you have trouble with some words, it may be fun for you to try this.

Look at the word. Spell it out loud. Then turn your back on the word. Take a deep breath and spell the word three times in a row. Have a friend listen to make sure you spell it correctly.

WRITE NOW!

Here are four more words with /ŏ/:
cannot rocks want watch
Use two of the words in a mystery story about a missing watch. You might begin: The last time I saw my watch was . . .

Lesson 20 Words with /ō/

Listen for /ō/ as you say each word.

hope

alone

whole

hole

close

joke

wrote

slow

know

yellow

blow

snow

show

goes

toe

November

1. Which two words sound exactly alike but are not spelled alike?

_____

2. Which word begins with the letter g?

_____

3. Write six words that end with the letter w but not the sound /w/.

_____

_____

_____

4. Write two words that begin with the letter w but not the sound /w/.

_____

5. Write three words that have more than one syllable. _____

_____

6. Which word begins with the letter j?

_____

7. Which word begins with /k/? _____

8. Which word ends with the last two letters of woe? _____

9. Which word ends with /p/? _____

Checkpoint

Write a spelling word for each clue.
Then use the Checkpoint Study Plan on page 224.

1. The color of the sun is ____.

2. Another word for play or program is ____.

3. The month before December is ____.

4. When you're sure about something, you ____.

5. Your foot has a big ____.

6. When there's no one else around, you are ____.

7. In summer we get rain, in winter we get ____.

8. To wish for something is to ____.

9. All the pieces together make a ____.

10. The opposite of fast is ____.

11. To make a candle go out, you ____.

12. A word for moves along is ____.

13. With your shovel you dig a ____.

14. The opposite of far away is ____.

15. The past tense of write is ____.

16. This mystery word comes from the Latin word *jocus*. Both the English and the French borrowed the word *jocus* and changed it. The French changed it to *jugleor*, which means juggler. A juggler is a person who does funny things. The English changed *jocus* to the mystery word. The mystery word means a funny story. Can you guess it? ____

Use each word once to complete this story.

WHAT ARE FRIENDS FOR?

Peter _____ a note to Jacob. Peter said he wanted to be _____. Jacob knew Peter was sad because his dog had run away. He decided to go see Peter anyway.

Jacob had a plan. He would tell a funny _____. He would make Peter laugh if it took the _____ day to do it.

"Why did the boy _____ the door and leave his father out in the month of _____?" Jacob asked.

Peter didn't answer. He stared at his dog's picture. "Because he wanted cold pop." Jacob laughed. Peter didn't even smile.

Jacob asked, "What kind of nail hurts when you hit it?" Peter didn't look up.

"A _____ nail." Jacob smiled. Peter didn't. Jacob tried again. "What comes after a snowstorm?" Peter didn't answer. Jacob said, "_____ shovels. Here is another one. What _____ away when you fill it up?"

"I wish you would go away," Peter said.

Jacob was hurt. He tried not to _____

it. He knew Peter was hurting, too. So he said, "A

_____. What did the north wind say to the

west wind?"

"I don't _____," said Peter.

Jacob told him the answer anyway. "It's time to

_____."

"I _____ you don't have any more

awful jokes," Peter said.

Jacob gave up. He ran out the door. Peter

yelled, "Jacob, _____ down."

Jacob slipped on a banana peel. He flew up in

the air and landed in a pile of bright red and

_____ leaves. All Peter could see

was Jacob's nose. Peter laughed and laughed.

Peter wiped his eyes and said, "Thanks for

making me laugh."

Jacob smiled and said, "That's what friends are

for, Peter."

hope
alone
whole
hole
close
joke
wrote
slow
know
yellow
blow
snow
show
goes
toe
November

Verbs

A verb is a word that expresses action.

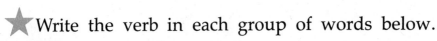

jumped   laughed   sat   sang

⭐ Write the verb in each group of words below.

1. wrote   whole   house

2. November   road   hope

3. ago   goes   hello

4. yellow   most   know

⭐ Unscramble the spelling words as you write each sentence below. Then circle the verbs.

5. John hurt his oet.

6. Please wosh me your new sneakers.

7. nows fell all night long.

8. We ate the lewoh pizza.

9. Krista bought a loweyl skateboard.

10. They dug a lohe in the yard.

AFTER THE TEST...

1. Did you spell all the words on your test correctly? _____

   If you did, go on to WRITE NOW! If you missed a word, it is important to know why.

2. Did you forget to write <u>ow</u> at the end of a word? _____

3. Did you forget to capitalize the first letter of <u>November</u>? _____

4. Did you write <u>hole</u> instead of <u>whole</u>? _____

5. If you made some other mistake, what was it? _____

6. Write the words you missed.

   _____

   _____

   _____

NOW WHAT ?

Some people learn best by writing a word. If you have trouble with some spelling words, it may be fun to try this.

Write your word four times in a row. Don't take your pencil off the paper until you are finished. Then close your eyes and spell the word four times in a row.

WRITE NOW!

Here are four more words with /ō/:

low homes nose own

Pretend you are flying in an airplane. Use two of these words to tell what you see on the ground.

Lesson 21 Words with /ō/

Listen for /ō/ as you say each word.

both

ago

almost

hold

comb

gold

hello

open

most

over

road

toast

loaf

boat

cocoa

coat

1. Write two words that begin with the letter o.

_____ _____

2. Write the word in which you see the letter b but don't hear /b/. _____

3. In which two-syllable word are both syllables pronounced /kō/? _____

4. Write three words that end with the letters st.

_____

_____

5. Which three words end with a vowel?

_____

_____

6. Write the two words that end with the letters ld. _____

7. Write a word that ends with the letters th.

_____

8. Write two words that end with the last three letters of goat.

_____

9. Write six words in which the letters oa spell /ō/.

_____

Checkpoint

Write a spelling word for each clue.
Then use the Checkpoint Study Plan on page 224.

1. To keep something in your hand is to ——.

2. Bread that is baked in one big pan is a ——.

3. Something you wear to keep warm in is a ——.

4. When you meet someone, you say ——.

5. Arrange your hair with a brush and a ——.

6. A yellow metal used to make rings is ——.

7. "Nearly, but not quite" means ——.

8. You put butter, jam, or jelly on ——.

9. The opposite of closed is ——.

10. Something to sail in is a ——.

11. The opposite of under is ——.

12. Another word for street is ——.

13. "Not one but two" means ——.

14. The opposite of least is ——.

15. "In the past" means ——.

16. Sometimes a new word comes from misspelling an old word. This mystery word names a food we often add to milk. The food comes from the beans of a tree. The tree is called the *cacao* tree. At first this food was called *cacao*. But many people misspelled *cacao*. Can you guess the word? ——

Use each word once to complete this story.

Fool's Paradise

Last summer we went to a lake that had an island in the middle of it. The island was tiny. It was called Fool's Paradise. There was a legend about the island. Many years _____ a treasure was buried there. The treasure was never found.

My sister Devon was excited about the legend. One day she packed a _____ of bread and some cheese. Then she got in a _____ and rowed to the island. Devon was going to comb every inch of it until she found the treasure.

Devon had been gone _____ three hours when a storm came up. Mom and Dad _____ were worried. So was I. Devon can take care of herself _____ of the time. But this was the worst storm I had ever seen.

Just then, Devon came running down the _____ to our cabin. "_____!" she yelled, as she came inside, dripping water all _____ everything.

"Change those wet clothes and _____ your hair," Dad said.

114

I said I would make some _____

and _____ .

"Wait," said Devon. "The storm blew over a tree on the island. I found something buried under it." She reached into her _____ pockets. "Close your eyes and _____ out your hands." We thought she was crazy. But we did it. Devon put rocks into our hands.

"Okay," she said, "_____ your eyes."

The rocks looked just like _____ . Then Mother said, "Oh, Devon. You've fallen for an old trick. That's only fool's gold."

Devon hadn't found a treasure. She had only found rocks that looked like gold. But now we know why the island is called Fool's Paradise.

both
ago
almost
hold
comb
gold
hello
open
most
over
road
toast
loaf
boat
cocoa
coat

Synonyms

Words that have the same meaning, or almost the same meaning, are called <u>synonyms</u>.

Hello   Howdy   Welcome   Hi

⭐Find a synonym from the spelling list for each word in the crossword puzzle. Then write the synonym clues for the puzzle.

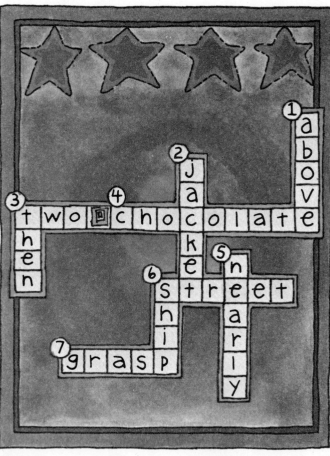

ACROSS

3. _____

4. _____

6. _____

7. _____

DOWN

1. _____

2. _____

3. _____

5. _____

6. _____

Hooray! You finished. Here's a synonym toast for you.

Good luck!   CONGRATULATIONS!   Salud!   Prosit!

(Spanish)   (German)

AFTER THE TEST . . .

1. Did you spell all the words on your test correctly? _____

   If you did, go on to WRITE NOW! If you missed a word, it is important to know why.

2. Did you forget the letter <u>b</u> at the end of <u>comb</u>? _____

3. Did you forget the letter <u>a</u> at the end of <u>cocoa</u>? _____

4. Did you put an extra letter in <u>almost</u>? _____

5. If you made some other mistake, what was it? _____

6. Write the words you missed.

   _____

   _____

NOW WHAT ?

Some people learn to spell by hearing a word spelled in a whisper. If you have trouble with some spelling words, it may be fun for you to try this.

Whisper each word over and over until you can spell it. It helps to find a quiet place to do this.

WRITE NOW!

Here are four more words with /ō/:
coast told goat growing
Use three of these words to write a funny story about an animal that kept getting bigger and bigger. You might want to begin: At first no one thought about how much Nanny ate . . .

117

Lesson 22 Words with /o͝o/

Listen for /o͝o/ as you say each word.

book

cookies

took

stood

wood

poor

foot

cook

shook

put

full

pull

sure

should

could

would

1. Which two words sound exactly alike but are not spelled alike?

_____ _____

2. Write three words in which you see the letter l but don't hear /l/. _____

_____

3. In which word does the letter s spell /sh/?

_____

4. Write four words that end with the last three letters of look.

_____ _____

_____ _____

5. In which word do you hear two syllables?

_____

6. Write three words that begin with the letter p.

_____ _____

_____

7. Which two words end with the last three letters of good?

_____ _____

8. Write two words that begin with the letter f.

_____

Checkpoint

Write a spelling word for each clue.
Then use the Checkpoint Study Plan on page 224.

1. We baked cakes, pies, and ____.

2. If you know for certain, you know for ____.

3. "To place" means to ____.

4. In a game of tug of war, take a rope and ____.

5. When you got up on your feet, you ____.

6. When you can't hold any more, you're ____.

7. "Ought to" means ____.

8. The opposite of rich is ____.

9. The past tense of shake is ____.

10. Today I can, yesterday I ____.

11. The past tense of take is ____.

12. Today I will, yesterday I ____.

13. To heat food on a stove is to ____.

14. You wear your shoe on your ____.

15. The trunk of a tree is made of ____.

16. Did you ever wonder what people wrote on before paper was invented? In England, people peeled bark off beech trees. The Old English word for beech was *bok.* When paper was invented, people stopped writing on bark. Instead, they tied papers together and wrote on them. They called this thing by a name that comes from the word *bok.* Can you guess the mystery word? ____

Use each word once to complete this story.

THE LITTLE MOUSE

Morris, the mouse, peeked over the top of

the _____ pile. The lion was asleep.

Then he saw the chocolate _____

beside the lion's left _____ .

Morris wondered if he _____ try

to get one of the cookies. The little mouse was very

hungry. He decided to take the chance.

Morris tiptoed over to the lion. He reached out

to _____ the cookies toward him. Whack!

The lion _____ his big foot down on the little

mouse. The lion _____ up and roared.

Morris was scared. He _____ like a leaf.

Morris thought fast. He said, "Mr. Lion, I'm just

a _____ little mouse. You would have to

build a fire to _____ me. Are you really

_____ I would be worth the trouble?"

The lion thought about it. He was still very

_____ from his last meal. So the lion told

the mouse to hurry away before he changed his

mind. Morris thanked him and was gone.

120

The next day, two hunters were looking for big game. They had read in a _____ that there were lots of lions in this country. The hunters saw the sleeping lion. They _____ out a net and threw it over him. There was nothing the lion _____ do except yell for help.

Morris heard the lion's cry. He looked until he found the lion. He said he _____ try to help. The lion said, "You are too small to help."

Morris didn't answer. He began to nibble on the net with his sharp teeth. Soon the little mouse had made a big hole. The lion was free.

That is how the lion learned that good things often come in small packages.

book
cookies
took
stood
wood
poor
foot
cook
shook
put
full
pull
sure
should
could
would

Capitals

The names of cities and states always begin with a capital letter.

New York City is the largest city in this country.
Phoenix is the capital of Arizona.

★ Unscramble the spelling words as you write each sentence. Put capital letters where they belong.

1. many dowo products come from maine.

2. you can put your otfo in four states at once: new mexico, utah, colorado, and arizona.

3. the rues winner for the largest state is alaska.

4. everyone dosluh visit chicago, illinois.

5. dowlu you like to go to new orleans?

6. san francisco ohsko during an earthquake.

7. i live in (fill in your town or city), (fill in your state).

8. my state capital is (fill in name).

Here are the ways /o͞o/ is spelled in this lesson: **oo, u, ou.**

AFTER THE TEST . . .

1. Did you spell all the words on your test correctly? _____

   If you did, go on to WRITE NOW! If you missed a word, it is important to know why.

2. Did you leave a letter out of <u>cookies</u>? _____

3. Did you put letters in the wrong order? _____

4. Did you put an extra letter in a word? _____

5. If you made some other mistake, what was it? _____

6. Write the words you missed.

   _____

   _____

NOW WHAT ?

It helps some people to see a word written. If you have trouble with some words, try this.

Write the word in the middle of a piece of paper. Look at it until you can spell it. Then fold both ends of the paper into the middle so the word is covered. Write the word three times. Check yourself by opening the "door."

WRITE NOW!

Here are four more words with /o͞o/:

   hood   looks   your   yourself

Use two of these words to describe a new jacket that you would like to buy for next winter.

123

Lesson 23 Adding ed and ing

Say each word.

closed

hoped

liked

sneezed

pleased

stopped

jogged

dropped

taking

smiling

driving

shining

beginning

hopping

dropping

shopping

Complete the word equations.

1. like   − e + ed = _____

2. hope   − e + ed = _____

3. close   − e + ed = _____

4. please   − e + ed = _____

5. sneeze − e + ed = _____

6. take   − e + ing = _____

7. drive   − e + ing = _____

8. smile   − e + ing = _____

9. shine   − e + ing = _____

10. jog   + g + ed = _____

11. stop   + p + ed = _____

12. drop   + p + ed = _____

13. hop   + p + ing = _____

14. drop   + p + ing = _____

15. shop   + p + ing = _____

16. begin   + n + ing = _____

Answer this question.

17. In which four words do the letters <u>ed</u> spell /t/?

_____

124

Checkpoint

Write a spelling word for each clue.
Then use the Checkpoint Study Plan on page 224.

1. The start is the ___.

2. Someone who had a cold coughed and ___.

3. If you wished for something, you ___.

4. "Letting something fall" means ___.

5. When the sun is bright, the sun is ___.

6. Another word for grinning is ___.

7. The opposite of started is ___.

8. Another word for happy is ___.

9. "Let fall" means ___.

10. Another word for enjoyed is ___.

11. The opposite of giving is ___.

12. Making a car go is ___.

13. The opposite of open is ___.

14. Kangaroos are always ___.

15. "Ran slowly" means ___.

16. Long ago in England there were places called
schoppes. A *schoppe* was a booth in a marketplace.
People sold things there. There is a verb that
means to buy things in a *schoppe*. It comes from
the word *schoppe* itself. This verb plus <u>ing</u> makes
the mystery word. Can you guess it? ___

Use each word once to complete this story.

SUMMER DAYS

Tim and his brother Lester _____ summer vacation. But it was already the _____ of August. They wanted something new to do.

The sun was _____ brightly. It was a hot day. The boys spent the morning looking for something to do. They had _____ to find a job.

By one o'clock they had given up. Nobody needed their help.

Tim and Lester were sitting on the front steps of their house when their dad opened the door. He was _____ into town. Dad was _____ the car to be fixed and was going _____ for food.

Dad asked, "Do you want to come along?" The boys shook their heads no. Dad understood the boys wanted to be alone.

He said, "Just keep looking. You can't expect a job to fall out of the sky." He _____ the door and left.

Tim started _____ up and down. "Look at the field, Lester. It's raining paper!"

Sure enough, paper was _____ out of a helicopter.

At first the boys _____ toward the field. But as they got closer, they ran.

As the papers _____ to the ground, Lester caught one. He started to laugh. He laughed so hard he started to sneeze. Lester always _____ when he laughed. Tim started laughing, too. The paper said:

Dirty Dan's Clean-up Crew

We will be _____ to clean up anything. If you have a mess, just call 555-5555.

P.S.   Need a job? We'll pay 10¢ for every 100

pieces of paper you pick up.

Dirty Dan

Finally, Lester and Tim _____ laughing. Now they were _____ from ear to ear. They had found jobs at last.

closed
hoped
liked
sneezed
pleased
stopped
jogged
dropped
taking
smiling
driving
shining
beginning
hopping
dropping
shopping

Commas

To make it easy to read a date, put a comma between the day and the year because they are different numbers.

July 4, 1776

 Write the dates below. Put in the commas.

1. March 23   1976 _____

2. December 27   1972 _____

3. Today's month, day, and year are _____.

4. I was born on _____.

 Write the sentences below. Use one of these spelling words to finish each sentence. Put commas where they belong.

jogged   closed
dropped   hoped

5. School ___ for vacation on June 23   1980.

_____

6. On January 25   1978, Lisa's mom ___ in a six-mile race.

_____

_____

7. Old friends ___ in to visit us on February 4   1980.

_____

_____

8. Jana ___ the party would be on May 17   1982.

_____

_____

128

Wrap Up  ★★★

LESSON 23

AFTER THE TEST . . .

1. Did you spell all the words on your test correctly? _____
   If you did, go on to WRITE NOW! If you missed a word, it is important to know why.

2. Did you forget to double the final consonant before adding <u>ed</u> or <u>ing</u>? _____

3. Did you forget to drop the final <u>e</u> before adding <u>ed</u> or <u>ing</u>? _____

4. Did you put an extra letter in a word? _____

5. If you made some other mistake, what was it? _____

6. Write the words you missed.

   _____

   _____

NOW WHAT ?

It helps some people to see a word written. If you have trouble with some words, try this.

Write your word in fancy letters. (You can decorate the letters, too.) Cover the word with your hand. Now write the word as you say each letter out loud. Do this until you can spell the words.

WRITE NOW!

Here are four more words with the <u>ed</u> or <u>ing</u> ending:
getting joking hopped hoping

Plan a surprise party for a friend. Use two of these words to write a paragraph about your plans.

Lesson 24 Words in Review

A. socks

bottom

wash

B. wrote

know

yellow

goes

November

C. comb

hello

road

cocoa

D. cookies

shook

sure

should

★ Use a piece of paper for the starred activities.

1. In Lesson 19 you studied two ways to spell /ŏ/: **o, a.** Write the words in list A.

_____

_____

2. In Lesson 20 you studied four ways to spell /ō/: **o_e, ow, oe, o.** Write the words in list B.

_____

_____

_____

★ **3.** Now write a sentence for each review word in lists A and B.

4. In Lesson 21 you studied two ways to spell /ō/: **o, oa.** Write the words in list C.

_____

_____

5. In Lesson 22 you studied three ways to spell /ŏŏ/ **oo, u, ou.** Write the words in list D.

_____

_____

★ **6.** Now write the review words in lists C and D. Look up each word in the Spelling Dictionary and write the guide words at the top of the page for each word.

★ **7.** Now write the words in lists A and B in alphabetical order.

Proof It Yourself

The sentences below have been proofread. The proofreading marks tell you what mistakes have to be corrected.

- _sp_ means that the word is misspelled.
- = means that a letter should be a capital.

Does it ever (sno) in florida?

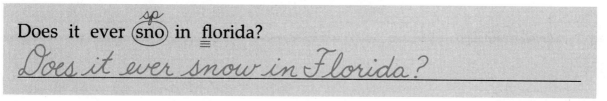

Does it ever snow in Florida?

Write the sentences correctly. Use each sentence to begin a paragraph. Write each paragraph on another paper. Proofread your work.

1. my (problum) (wuz) that I needed more time to finish.

_____

_____

2. This is a joke I (rote) last november.

_____

_____

3. we took a (bote) ride in florida and saw a huge alligator.

_____

_____

4. we (shud) have put sugar instead of salt in the (cokies).

_____

_____

5. jim (likt) the beginning of this book better than the end.

_____

_____

Lesson 25 /o͞o/ and /yo͞o/

Listen for /o͞o/ or /yo͞o/ as you say each word.

noon

school

too

tooth

blue

true

Tuesday

who

move

two

news

knew

June

July

★

few

used

1. Write the five words in which you see the letter <u>w</u> but don't hear /w/. _____

_____

2. Which three words are always spelled with a capital letter? _____

_____

3. Which four words have double vowels? _____

_____

4. Which two words end with the last two letters of <u>glue</u>? _____

_____

5. Write three words that have the letters <u>ew</u>. _____

_____

6. Write three words in which you hear /z/ but don't see the letter <u>z</u>. _____

_____

7. Which word ends with the sound /v/? _____

Checkpoint

Write a spelling word for each clue.
Then use the Checkpoint Study Plan on page 224.

1. The opposite of false is ___.

2. The month that comes before August is ___.

3. In newspapers you can read the ___.

4. The dentist pulled her baby ___.

5. One plus one is ___.

6. To go from one place to another is to ___.

7. A place where people go to learn is a ___.

8. The opposite of many is ___.

9. The time of day for eating lunch is ___.

10. Another word for also is ___.

11. Something that is useful can be ___.

12. The month after May is ___.

13. The color of the sky is ___.

14. "What person" means ___.

15. Today I know, yesterday I ___.

16. Have you ever heard of the Vikings? They were people from northern Europe. The Vikings gave us our mystery word. The mystery word comes from the word *Tiwdaeg. Tiw* was the Old English name for the Viking war god. *Daeg* meant day. Can you guess which modern word comes from *Tiwdaeg?* ___

Use each word once to complete this story.

THE ALL-SCHOOL MARATHON

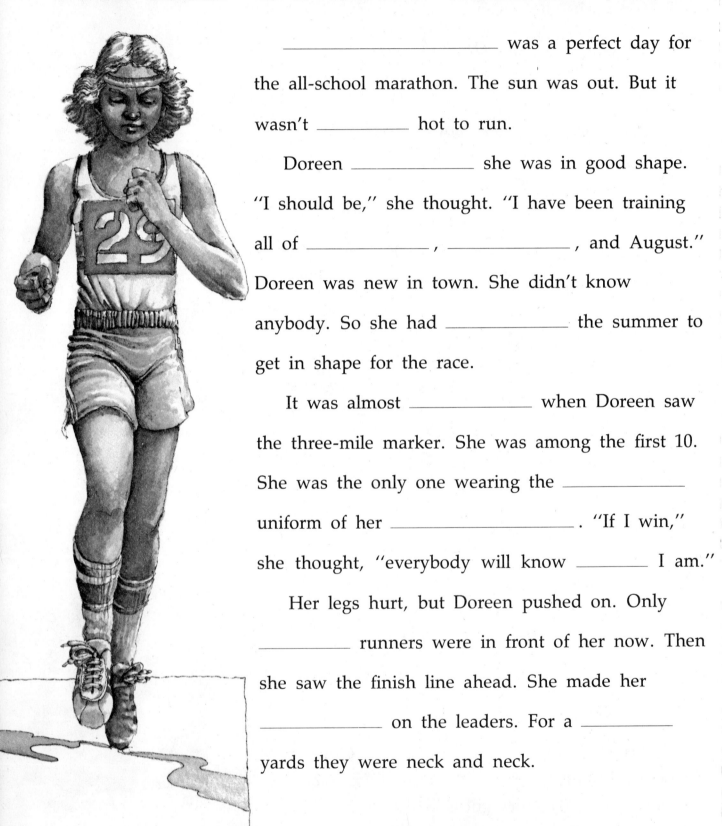

_____ was a perfect day for the all-school marathon. The sun was out. But it wasn't _____ hot to run.

Doreen _____ she was in good shape. "I should be," she thought. "I have been training all of _____, _____, and August." Doreen was new in town. She didn't know anybody. So she had _____ the summer to get in shape for the race.

It was almost _____ when Doreen saw the three-mile marker. She was among the first 10. She was the only one wearing the _____ uniform of her _____. "If I win," she thought, "everybody will know _____ I am."

Her legs hurt, but Doreen pushed on. Only _____ runners were in front of her now. Then she saw the finish line ahead. She made her _____ on the leaders. For a _____ yards they were neck and neck.

Without warning, Doreen tripped. She fell flat on her face. When she fell, she chipped a tooth. A crowd gathered around her.

"Did I win or lose?" she asked.

"You finished second," a boy said. "But I've got _____ for you. That's the first time our school ever came close to winning."

"It's _____," said somebody else. "You're the best runner we have ever had."

Doreen laughed. "Now everybody will know me," she said. "I'm the fast runner with the chipped _____!"

noon
school
too
tooth
blue
true
Tuesday
who
move
two
news
knew
June
July
few
used

Pronunciation

Words are not always pronounced the way they are spelled. The dictionary shows us how to say a word. The way a word is said is called its <u>pronunciation</u>. In a dictionary, the pronunciation is written as a sound spelling after the entry word.

Entry Word →

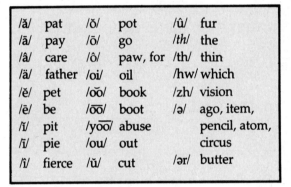

> **school** | skōōl | —*noun, plural* **schools**
> A place of teaching and learning: *We learned about Japan in school.*

Pronunciation Sound Spelling

The dictionary uses letters and symbols to write a sound spelling. These letters and symbols can be found in the <u>pronunciation key</u>.

/ă/	pat	/ŏ/	pot	/û/	fur
/ā/	pay	/ō/	go	/th/	the
/â/	care	/ô/	paw, for	/th/	thin
/ä/	father	/oi/	oil	/hw/	which
/ĕ/	pet	/ŏŏ/	book	/zh/	vision
/ē/	be	/ōō/	boot	/ə/	ago, item,
/ĭ/	pit	/yōō/	abuse		pencil, atom,
/ī/	pie	/ou/	out		circus
/î/	fierce	/ŭ/	cut	/ər/	butter

The <u>oo</u> in <u>school</u> sounds like the <u>oo</u> in <u>boot</u>.

★ Write the sample words from the pronunciation key for these sounds:

1. <u>oi</u> in <u>boil</u> _____   2. <u>o</u> in <u>closed</u> _____

3. <u>o</u> in <u>hot</u> _____   4. <u>a</u> in <u>taking</u> _____

★ Write the word that goes with each sound spelling below. Check your answers in the Spelling Dictionary.

tooth   July   Tuesday   few

5. /fyōō/ _____

6. /tōōth/ _____

7. /tōōz′ dē/ _____

8. /jōō lī′/ _____

136

LESSON 25

AFTER THE TEST . . .

1. Did you spell all the words on your test correctly? _____
   If you did, go on to WRITE NOW! If you missed a word, it is important to know why.

2. Did you forget to capitalize the first letter of <u>Tuesday</u>, <u>June</u>, or <u>July</u>? _____

3. Did you write <u>eu</u> instead of <u>ue</u>? _____

4. Did you write <u>too</u> instead of <u>two</u>? _____

5. If you made some other mistake, what was it? _____

6. Write the words you missed.

_____

_____

NOW WHAT ?

It helps some people to see a word in writing. If you have trouble with some spelling words, it may be fun to try this.

Write the word in big letters on a chalkboard. Then trace each letter with your finger. Say each letter as you trace it. Do this until your finger has erased the word.

WRITE NOW!

Here are four more words with /ōō/ or /yōō/:

moving   cool   doing   music

Use two of these words to write a story about a girl moving to a new town. You might begin: Marie didn't want to leave her friends. But her new house was . . .

Lesson 26 Words with /û/

Listen for /û/ as you say each word.

girl

bird

first

dirt

third

world

work

word

worm

curl

fur

Thursday

turn

learn

earth

were

1. Which three words have the letters <u>th</u>?

_____

_____

2. Write four words that begin with the first three letters of <u>worst</u>.

_____

_____

3. Which two words end with the letters <u>rn</u>?

_____

4. Write two words that end with the letter <u>l</u>.

_____   _____

5. Write two words that begin with the letter <u>f</u>.

_____   _____

6. Which two words end with vowels?

_____   _____

7. Write three words that end with the letters <u>rd</u>.

_____   _____

8. Which word begins and ends like <u>dart</u>?

_____

9. Which word always begins with a capital letter?

_____

Checkpoint

Write a spelling word for each clue.
Then use the Checkpoint Study Plan on page 224.

1. Something you have to wash off is ___.

2. Your chance means your ___.

3. "Coming before any others" means ___.

4. The planet you live on is the ___.

5. A job or task is ___.

6. Next after second is ___.

7. A cat is covered with ___.

8. Today they are, yesterday they ___.

9. Another word for the earth is the ___.

10. The day after Wednesday is ___.

11. A group of letters together is a ___.

12. A female child is a ___.

13. You go to school to ___.

14. Something you take fishing is a ___.

15. People sometimes change words to make them sound nicer. This is one reason spellings change. The two mystery words were once spelled *brid* and *crul*. They began with two consonants followed by a vowel. But people made the second consonant change places with the vowel. Can you guess how *brid* is spelled today? ___

16. How is *crul* spelled today? ___

THE BUNTING

Last _____ my class went to Lone Pine State Park for a nature walk. We take these trips to _____ about nature. And they are a fun part of our school _____. Each class trip is a holiday.

At the park a _____ named Jane said she would be our guide. She told us lots of facts about our planet, the _____. She told us what plants and animals to look for. Jane said that we might even see a painted bunting. That is a rare _____ with red, blue, and green feathers.

We _____ only a little way down the trail when showoff Bonnie Williams spotted a fawn. It had white spots on its _____. If only I could find something special, too!

I kept my eyes and ears open. The path turned once, twice, and then a _____ time . I happened to look down at the _____ behind a tall pine tree.

140

At _____ , I saw only a wiggly

_____ . I watched it _____ and

uncurl. Then I saw one of the most beautiful things

in the _____ . I saw a real live painted

bunting. I wanted to yell to the others, but I didn't

say a _____ . I didn't want to scare the

painted bunting.

I saw the bird _____ and fly away.
In a flash of color it was gone. No one else saw
the bunting. But I knew that I was one up on
showoff Bonnie Williams.

girl
bird
first
dirt
third
world
work
word
worm
curl
fur
Thursday
turn
learn
earth
were

Antonyms

An antonym is a word that means the opposite of another word.

An antonym of <u>small</u> is <u>big</u>.
An antonym of <u>thick</u> is <u>thin</u>.

★ Match each word below with its antonym.

under   add   huge   young

1. subtract _____   2. tiny _____

3. over _____   4. old _____

★ Each group of four words below has a pair of antonyms and a pair of synonyms. (Remember that synonyms are words that mean the same.) First write the antonyms together. Then write the synonyms together.

5. full   forever   empty   always

antonyms: _____

synonyms: _____

6. earth   first   world   last

antonyms: _____

synonyms: _____

7. study   learn   boy   girl

antonyms: _____

synonyms: _____

8. dirty   clean   bird   fowl

antonyms: _____

synonyms: _____

AFTER THE TEST . . .

1. Did you spell all the words on your test correctly? _____
   If you did, go on to WRITE NOW! If you missed a word, it is important to know why.

2. Did you leave a letter out of <u>earth</u>? _____

3. Did you forget to capitalize the first letter of <u>Thursday</u>? _____

4. Did you put the letters in the wrong order? _____

5. If you made some other mistake, what was it? _____

6. Write the words you missed.

   _____

   _____

   _____

NOW WHAT ?

It helps some people to hear a word spelled in a special way. If you have trouble with some words, it may be fun for you to try this.

Look at the word and practice spelling it. When you are ready, turn around. Take a deep breath. Spell the word three times without stopping. Ask a friend to listen as you spell the word.

WRITE NOW!

Here are four more words with /û/:
shirt return circus turned
Pretend you went to the circus.

Use two of these words to write a paragraph about the clowns you saw.

Lesson 27 Words with /ä/

Listen for /ä/ as you say each word.

father

market

barn

garden

star

sharp

bark

yard

dark

hard

card

start

March

arm

art

heart

1. Which two words begin with the letter <u>a</u>?

_____

2. Which word has the letters <u>th</u> in it?

_____

3. Which word is spelled with a capital letter?

_____

4. Write three words that have two syllables.

_____

_____

5. In which word is /ä/ spelled with the letters <u>ea</u>? _____

6. Which two words begin with the letters <u>st</u>?

_____

7. Which two words have the letters <u>ark</u> in them?

_____

8. Which three words end with the letters <u>ard</u>?

_____

9. Which word begins with the letters <u>sh</u>?

_____

10. Write two words that begin with the letter <u>b</u>.

Checkpoint

Write a spelling word for each clue.
Then use the Checkpoint Study Plan on page 224.

1. A place where you grow flowers is a ___.

2. Blood is pumped through your ___.

3. A point of light in the night sky is a ___.

4. A place where you buy things is a ___.

5. A short, gruff sound a dog makes is a ___.

6. On a friend's birthday, you send a ___.

7. Something that has an edge that cuts is ___.

8. The month that follows February is ___.

9. It takes three feet to make one ___.

10. A beautiful painting is ___.

11. A place where cows live is a ___.

12. When there is no light, it is ___.

13. Another word for begin is ___.

14. The opposite of easy is ___.

15. She is my mother, he is my ___.

16. Sometimes words that are spelled alike have different meanings. They are called homographs.
    This mystery word is two homographs. One homograph means a weapon. It comes from the Latin word *arma*. The other means a part of the body. It comes from the Old German word *aram*. Can you guess this word? ___

145

Annie Oakley

One of the great sharpshooters in Buffalo Bill's Wild West Show was Annie Oakley.

Annie was born on a farm in Ohio on August 13, 1860. Annie's mother and _____ noticed her interest in target shooting. But they never guessed that she would one day be a _____ in Buffalo Bill's show.

Annie grew up like most kids on a farm. She had to feed the animals that lived in the pens and in the _____. She had to pick the _____ vegetables. And she had to go

146

to the _____ to buy the things they

needed. But Annie also practiced sharpshooting.

Her father would set up cans in the front

_____ for shooting practice. A neighbor

watching Annie once said, "She could shoot the

_____ off a tree!" The neighbor was right.

Annie's good aim and her _____

eyesight made her a local star.

Annie put her whole _____ into her

work. She often practiced shooting until it was

_____ . But all her _____ work

helped her become a star.

On _____ 20, 1874, Annie won a

shooting contest against champion Frank E. Butler.

Later Annie and Frank got married. Then they

joined Buffalo Bill's show.

Buffalo Bill used Annie's sharpshooting act to

_____ the Wild West Show. One of her

most dangerous acts was shooting the thin edge of

a playing _____ . She did this while holding

a rifle in one _____ and hanging from a

moving horse with the other!

Annie thought sharpshooting was more than just

fancy shooting. She believed it was an _____ .

father
market
barn
garden
star
sharp
bark
yard
dark
hard
card
start
March
arm
art
heart

147

Definitions

The meaning of a word is called the <u>definition</u>. Some words have more than one meaning. <u>Heart</u> has two definitions in the Spelling Dictionary.

Definition 1 ⟶

> **heart** | härt | —*noun, plural* **hearts**
> **1.** The organ in the chest that pumps blood through the body: *The doctor listened to my heart.* **2.** Courage and enthusiasm: *Howard put his whole heart into winning the game.*

⟵ **Definition 2**

★ Read the sample sentences in the two definitions above. The words around the word <u>heart</u> give a clue to its meaning.

Which definition of <u>heart</u> is used in each sentence below?

1. Our class lost heart when we lost the game. _____

2. My heart beats fast after a race. _____

Some words in our language are spelled exactly like other words. But they became part of our language at different times. And they have different meanings. These words have raised numbers beside them in the dictionary.

> **bark**¹ | bärk | —*noun, plural* **barks** The sharp, explosive sound made by a dog or fox: *I could hear my dog's bark a mile away.* —*verb* To make the sharp sound a dog makes: *Fido likes to bark at cats.*
> **bark**² | bärk | —*noun, plural* **barks** The outer covering of trees and other woody plants: *The bark of a birch tree is thin and peels off easily.*

★ Which definition of <u>bark</u> is used in each sentence below?

3. Lassie has a loud bark. _____

4. My cat clawed the bark of the tree. _____

Wrap Up

LESSON 27

AFTER THE TEST...

1. Did you spell all the words on your test correctly? _____

   If you did, go on to WRITE NOW! If you missed a word, it is important to know why.

2. Did you forget to capitalize the first letter of the month <u>March</u>?

   _____

3. Did you leave a letter out of <u>heart</u>? _____

4. Did you put letters in the wrong order? _____

5. If you made some other mistake, what was it? _____

6. Write the words you missed.

   _____

   _____

NOW WHAT ?

Some people learn best by writing a word. If you have trouble with some spelling words, it may be fun to try this.

Draw a star. Write the word inside the star. Then stare at the word. When you can spell the word, color the star.

WRITE NOW!

Here are four more words with /ä/:

   car   parts   park   party

Use three of these words to tell your friends at school how to get to your house for your birthday.

Lesson 28 Words with /oi/

Listen for /oi/ as you say each word.

soil

broil

coin

point

boil

choice

noise

voice

spoil

oil

join

boy

toy

joy

enjoy

royal

1. Write the two words in which you hear /s/ but don't see the letter <u>s</u>.

_____

2. Which word ends with the letters <u>al</u>?

_____

3. Write the word in which you hear /z/ but don't see the letter <u>z</u>. _____

4. Write five words that have the letters <u>oil</u>.

_____   _____

_____   _____

_____

5. Which four words end with the last two letters of <u>decoy</u>?

_____   _____

_____   _____

6. Write three words that have the letters <u>oin</u>.

_____   _____

_____

7. Write the two words that begin with a vowel.

_____   _____

Checkpoint

Write a spelling word for each clue.
Then use the Checkpoint Study Plan on page 224.

1. To cook directly under or over heat is to ____.

2. Seeds are planted in ____.

3. Loud sounds make lots of ____.

4. Something you like is something you ____.

5. "Fit for a king or queen" means ____.

6. A liquid you need to run a car is ____.

7. To take part in something with others is to ____.

8. A penny, a dime, or a quarter is a ____.

9. The tip is the ____.

10. If you get to choose, you have a ____.

11. A male child is a ____.

12. To ruin is to ____.

13. Something you play with is a ____.

14. Another word for happiness is ____.

15. You talk and sing with your ____.

16. This mystery word tells what happens when liquid gets very hot. It comes from the Latin word *bulla*. *Bulla* meant bubble. When a liquid gets very hot, we can see large bubbles in it. The bubbles move about very quickly. When liquid gets hot and begins to bubble, it begins to ____.

Use each word once to complete this story.

A Camping Tale

Soon after May had caught the fish, she realized she was alone. She yelled until she almost lost her _____. But no one answered. She was lost. And there was no one to _____ the way. Her camping trip had become a nightmare.

"I might not _____ it," she thought, "but I guess I'll have to make it alone. I don't have any other _____!"

At first, May jumped at every _____ in the woods. But soon she got used to the noises.

May was very hungry. That made her think about the _____ purse in her pocket. But the coins might have been _____ money. They wouldn't buy any food in the woods. At least she had a sleeping bag and a few supplies. She would be all right.

"The first thing I'll do," she thought, "is build a fire. Then I'll _____ water for cocoa. I don't have any _____ to fry the fish. I'll have to _____ the fish I caught. I'll cook a _____ feast!"

May had just finished broiling the fish when it began to rain. She didn't want the rain to _____ her breakfast. She pushed a branch into the soft _____ . Then she put her sleeping bag over it to make a tent. It was warm inside. May began to yawn. Soon she was fast asleep.

When she woke up, a _____ was looking into the tent. "Breakfast is ready," said her brother. "Aren't you going to _____ us?"

May was in her family's tent. It was a bright morning. The birds were singing for _____ . She laughed. It was only a dream after all.

soil
broil
coin
point
boil
choice
noise
voice
spoil
oil
join
boy
toy
joy
enjoy
royal

Review of Capitals

Use a capital letter to begin:

- *the first word of a sentence* • *the word* <u>I</u>
- *the names of people and pets* • *the names of cities and states*
- *the names of streets*

⭐ Unscramble the spelling words as you write each sentence below. Put capital letters where they belong.

1. martha felt yloar on her birthday.

_____

2. i noyej visiting minneapolis.

_____

3. fido makes a lot of sonie!

_____

4. vincent has a good ocevi.

_____

5. can you tonip out mallory street?

_____

6. shall we robil this chicken?

_____

7. this nico was made in colorado.

_____

8. mrs. hays bought a yto for her baby oby.

_____

9. kevin and i want to nioj the team.

_____

Wrap Up

LESSON 28

AFTER THE TEST...

1. Did you spell all the words on your test correctly? _____

   If you did, go on to WRITE NOW! If you missed a word, it is important to know why.

2. Did you put the letters <u>oi</u> in the wrong order? _____

3. Did you put the letter <u>k</u> at the beginning of <u>coin</u>? _____

4. Did you put the wrong letters at the beginning of <u>enjoy</u>? ___

5. If you made some other mistake, what was it? _____

6. Write the words you missed.

   _____

   _____

   _____

NOW WHAT ?

It helps some people to hear a word spelled out loud. If you have trouble with some spelling words, it may be fun to try this.

Think of a sentence with the word in it. When you say the sentence, spell the word.

If you think this is too easy, try a sentence with two spelling words.

WRITE NOW!

Here are four more words with /oi/:
   boiled cowboy joined toys
Use two of the words to write a funny story about the Old West. You might begin: A stranger rode into town eating a doughnut.

Lesson 29 Contractions

Say each word.

hasn't

aren't

couldn't

didn't

doesn't

hadn't

haven't

mustn't

shouldn't

wasn't

weren't

isn't

wouldn't

won't

don't

can't

1. Which two words begin with /k/?

_____   _____

2. Write the three words that have the letters <u>ould</u>.

_____   _____

_____

3. Write the two words that begin with a vowel.

_____   _____

4. Write the two words that have the <u>o</u> spelling of

/ō/. _____   _____

5. Which word begins with the letter <u>m</u>?

_____

6. Which three words begin with the letter <u>h</u>?

_____   _____

_____

7. Which three words begin with the letter <u>d</u>?

_____   _____

_____

8. Which four words begin with the letter <u>w</u>?

_____   _____

_____

Checkpoint

Write a spelling word for each clue.
Then use the Checkpoint Study Plan on page 224.

1. are   + not = ___

2. did   + not = ___

3. had   + not = ___

4. has   + not = ___

5. was   + not = ___

6. is   + not = ___

7. does   + not = ___

8. have   + not = ___

9. must   + not = ___

10. were + not = ___

11. will + not = ___

12. do   + not = ___

13. would + not = ___

14. cannot   = ___

15. The first mystery word is a form of the verb can. It used to be spelled coud. This word plus the contraction of not is ___.

16. The second mystery word is a form of the verb shall. It used to be spelled sholde. The word plus the contraction of not is ___.

157

THE CHALLENGE

Billy watched Dave, waiting to see what he would do next. This was the first time he had faced Dave. Billy _____ happy about it. "If only I _____ said yes to his challenge," he thought. "Then I _____ be in this mess."

"You _____ going to back down?" Dave asked. Billy knew that he could not back down now. He just _____ back down. A lot of his friends were watching him. They _____ going to leave until it was all over. They had tried to tell him about Dave. "You _____ heard?" they had asked. "He's tough. He _____ like losing."

Billy _____ like to lose either. His hands were sweaty. His knees were shaking. "I _____ help it," he thought. "I want to beat this guy." Billy rubbed his hands on his clothes. "Be steady," he told himself. "If there is one thing I must not do, I _____ look scared.

158

I _____ want to make it easy for Dave to win. Besides, it _____ be the end of the world if I lose."

Then Dave made his move. Billy knew that it was the wrong one. "He _____ got a chance now," he thought.

Billy grinned. "You _____ have done that, Dave," he said. "I'm going to beat you. But don't worry. It _____ going to hurt for long."

In one move, Billy cleared the checkerboard of Dave's pieces. The game was over. Billy had met the challenge.

hasn't
aren't
couldn't
didn't
doesn't
hadn't
haven't
mustn't
shouldn't
wasn't
weren't
isn't
wouldn't
won't
don't
can't

Apostrophes

A contraction is a shortened form of two words. An apostrophe (') in a contraction shows that a letter or letters have been left out.

<u>Two Words</u>	<u>Contraction</u>	<u>Left Out</u>
are not	*aren't*	*o*
is not	*isn't*	*o*

★ Write the contractions of the words in the list below.

1. could not _____

2. have not _____

3. do not _____

4. had not _____

★ Write two sentences using the contractions <u>wouldn't</u> and <u>won't</u>.

5. wouldn't _____

6. won't _____

7. What are the two words for <u>wouldn't</u>? _____

8. What are the two words for <u>won't</u>? _____

★ Write the correct contraction in each sentence.

9. Sasha (wasn't/weren't) home yesterday.

_____

10. My other friends (wasn't/weren't) home either!

_____

★ Sometimes a contraction is made from one word.

11. What is the one word from which <u>can't</u> is

made?

Wrap Up

LESSON 29

AFTER THE TEST . . .

1. Did you spell all the words on your test correctly? _____
If you did, go on to WRITE NOW! If you missed a word, it is important to know why.

2. Did you forget an apostrophe (')?
_____

3. Did you put an apostrophe in the wrong place? _____

4. Did you leave out a letter?
_____

5. If you made some other mistake, what was it? _____

6. Write the words you missed.
_____

NOW WHAT ?

Some people learn best by saying a word out loud. If you have trouble with some spelling words, it may be fun to try this.

Spell each contraction you missed out loud. But clap your hands where the apostrophe (') should be. Do this until you can spell each word three times in a row without a mistake.

WRITE NOW!

Here are some words without contractions:

should not   does not
will not   do not

Invent a machine that will set the table and wash the dishes. Use two of these sets of words to tell people how to use your machine.

Lesson 30 Words in Review

A. tooth
true
move
knew
July
few
used

B. dirt
worm
curl
learn
were

C. sharp
heart

D. voice
enjoy

★ Use a piece of paper for the starred activities.

1. In Lesson 25 you studied five ways to spell /o͞o/: **oo, ue, o, ew, u**. And you studied two ways to spell /yo͞o/: **ew, u_e**. Write the words in list A.

2. In Lesson 26 you studied five ways to spell /û/: **i, o, u, ea, e**. Write the words in list B.

★**3.** Now write the words in lists A and B. Look them up in the Spelling Dictionary and write the sound spelling next to each word.

4. In Lesson 27 you studied two ways to spell /ä/ **a, ea**. Write the words in list C.

5. In Lesson 28 you studied two ways to spell /oi/: **oi, oy**. Write the words in list D.

★**6.** Now write a sentence for each review word in lists C and D.

★**7.** Write sentences for the words in lists A and B.

★**8.** Write all the review words in alphabetical order.

162

Proof It Yourself

The sentences below have been proofread. The proofreading marks tell you what mistakes have to be corrected.

- *sp* means that the word is misspelled.
- ＝ means that a letter should be a capital.

I saw mr. Marks at the (markit).

I saw Mr. Marks at the market.

Write the sentences correctly. Use each sentence to begin a paragraph. Write each paragraph on another paper. Proofread your work.

1. charlie (new) that (Toosday) would be the best day of his life!

_____

_____

2. I was the (thurd) one mrs. roper picked for the school show.

_____

_____

3. My (farther) is taking cindy and me to his store in dallas.

_____

_____

4. When i heard my (voyse) on the tape, i had to smile.

_____

_____

5. I (wownt) be living on state st. after next month.

_____

_____

Lesson 31 Words with /ô/

Listen for /ô/ as you say each word.

autumn

August

born

fork

morning

sport

popcorn

storm

north

corner

before

door

floor

pour

four

quart

1. Which word begins with /kw/?

_____

2. Write two words that begin with a vowel.

_____

3. Which two words end with the last three

letters of <u>tour</u>?

_____

4. Write three words that begin with the letter <u>f</u>.

_____

5. Write four words that have the letters <u>orn</u>.

_____

_____

6. Which word ends with the letters <u>th</u>?

_____

7. Which word begins with a consonant and ends

with a vowel? _____

8. Write two words that begin with the letter <u>s</u>.

_____

9. Which two words end with the letters <u>oor</u>?

_____

10. Which word always begins with a capital letter?

Checkpoint

Write a spelling word for each clue.
Then use the Checkpoint Study Plan on page 224.

1. You eat breakfast in the ___.

2. The kind of corn you eat at the movies is ___.

3. The place where two streets meet is the ___.

4. Your birthday is the day you were ___.

5. Another name for the season fall is ___.

6. Outside is the ground, inside is the ___.

7. Strong winds and rain are a ___.

8. To get into a room, you open the ___.

9. The opposite of south is ___.

10. The number after three is ___.

11. To put milk into a glass is to ___.

12. Another word for game is ___.

13. Two pints make one ___.

14. You eat with a knife, spoon, and ___.

15. The opposite of after is ___.

16. Perhaps the greatest Roman emperor was
Caesar Augustus. *Augustus* meant "very great
man." Caesar Augustus made sure that he
would always be remembered. He had the
Romans name a certain month after him. This
month still has his name. Guess it, and you
will know the mystery word. ___

The Land of Flipflop

In the Land of Flipflop, everything is backward. People bite mosquitoes. Cars are pulled by horses. Singing cows give one _____ of blue milk every day. The sun comes out at night. And the stars come out every _____.

Red snow falls in _____ when it's hot. Flowers bloom when the leaves fall in _____. South is _____, of course. And <u>after</u> means _____.

SNAP!

Two plus two equals zero. Two minus two equals

_____ . Of course.

People don't eat buttered _____

in the movies. They nibble on buttered mud. A knife

is used to eat potatoes. Barbecued barracuda is cut

with a _____ . It seems right to Flipflopians.

Children take care of their parents. And when

the parents are bad, they don't have to sit in a

_____ . They stand on the roof. All

over Flipflop there are moms and dads on rooftops!

You can't go from room to room inside the

houses. No wall has a _____ to walk

through. The beds are on the ceiling. And the

pictures hang on the _____ .

Baseball played under water in snowsuits is the

favorite _____ .

When the green rain falls and the big winds

blow, it's not a _____ . In Flipflop,

that's a nice day. But when the sun comes out,

they say, "It's beginning to _____ ."

Grandmothers and grandfathers grow young.

Babies are _____ old. And Flipflop is

everywhere because there's no such place as

nowhere.

autumn
August
born
fork
morning
sport
popcorn
storm
north
corner
before
door
floor
pour
four
quart

Alphabetical Order

Put words that begin with the same letter into alphabetical order by using the second letter.

h<u>a</u>mmer   h<u>o</u>rse

The letter <u>a</u> comes before <u>o</u>, so <u>hammer</u> comes before <u>horse</u>.

Sometimes the first and second letters of a word are the same. When this happens, use the third letter to put words in alphabetical order.

tr<u>a</u>in   tr<u>i</u>m

The letter <u>a</u> comes before <u>i</u>, so <u>train</u> comes before <u>trim</u>.

★ Look at the third letter of each word in the lists below. Then write the words in alphabetical order.

1. **autumn   aunt   August**

_____

_____

_____

2. **fork   four   foggy**

_____

_____

_____

★ Put the words below each sentence in alphabetical order. Then write the sentence using those words.

3. Ray ____ weeks learning the ____ of jogging last ____.

   (sport, spent, spring) _____

_____

4. ____ ____ ran two minutes ____ she ____ to fall ____.

   (began, Beatrice, before, behind, Becker) _____

168

AFTER THE TEST...

1. Did you spell all the words on your test correctly? _____

   If you did, go on to WRITE NOW! If you missed a word, it is important to know why.

2. Did you forget the letter <u>e</u> at the end of <u>before</u>? _____

3. Did you forget the letter <u>u</u> in <u>qu</u>art? _____

4. Did you forget to capitalize the first letter of <u>August</u>? _____

5. If you made some other mistake, what was it? _____

6. Write the words you missed.

   _____

   _____

   _____

NOW WHAT?

It helps some people to see a word. If you have trouble with some spelling words, it may be fun for you to try this.

Write the word four times. But write it a different way each time. Say each letter as you write the word. Do this until you can spell the word.

WRITE NOW!

Here are four more words with /ô/:

soft fourteen horses order

Use two of these words to make a poster for a rodeo.

Lesson 32 Words with /ô/

Listen for /ô/ as you say each word.

frog

long

along

off

belong

strong

water

always

mall

tall

talk

walk

bought ·

brought

draw

because

1. Write the two words in which you hear /z/ but don't see the letter z.

_____ _____

2. Write the two words in which you see the letter l but don't hear /l/.

_____ _____

3. Write three words that have double consonants.

ff _____ ll _____

ll _____

4. Write the two words in which you see the letters gh but don't hear them.

_____ _____

5. Write four words that end with the letters ng.

_____ _____

_____ _____

6. Write two words that begin with the letter w.

_____ _____

7. Which word begins with the letters fr?

_____

8. Which word ends with the letter w but not the sound /w/? _____

Checkpoint

Write a spelling word for each clue.
Then use the Checkpoint Study Plan on page 224.

1. If you go with someone, you tag ___.

2. To make a picture is to ___.

3. Something you do with your voice is ___.

4. The liquid you find in an ocean or pond is ___.

5. A place with many shops is a ___.

6. A small green animal that hops is a ___.

7. "How high" means the same as how ___.

8. Put things where they ___.

9. "Carried something here" means ___.

10. A ruler is 12 inches ___.

11. "Paid for something" means ___.

12. The opposite of never is ___.

13. The opposite of on is ___.

14. To go on foot is to ___.

15. The opposite of weak is ___.

16. Some words are often used together. This word
    took the place of three words. They are <u>by</u>,
    <u>cause</u>, and <u>that</u>. People used to say that a dish
    broke by cause that it fell. Later, they made
    one word of <u>by</u> and <u>cause</u> and stopped saying
    <u>that</u>. Today we say that a dish broke ___ it fell.
    Guess the word.

THE FROG PRINCE

Use each word once to complete this story.

Marci's brother Ben liked to _____ pictures. One day he drew a picture of a green _____. It had a little crown on its head. Ben _____ the picture to Marci.

Ben was deaf. So Ben and Marci used their hands to talk to each other. "If you kiss a frog, it will turn into a prince," Ben signed to Marci with his hands. She was sure he was grinning at her.

"That's just silly _____," Marci signed back. But soon she began to think about a frog turning into a handsome prince. He was six feet _____. His _____ hands held the reins of a horse. A _____ sword hung at his side.

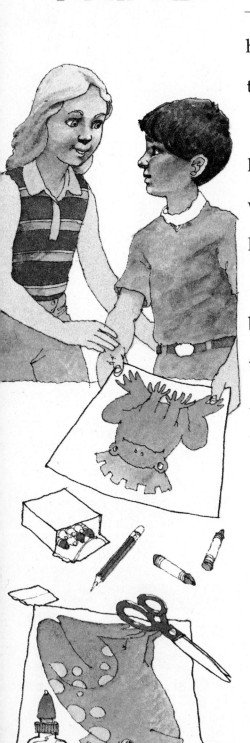

"Aren't you ready yet?" her mother called. Marci's dream ended.

Every Saturday, Marci's mother went shopping at the _____. Marci _____ went. Ben usually came _____, too. Today, Mother and Ben _____ food. Marci wanted to be by herself. She went for a _____.

172

It was warm. So Marci took _____ her coat. But she was still hot.

She walked to the pond in the center of the mall. "Maybe it's cooler by the _____," she thought. Marci sat down on the wall. Suddenly a frog jumped from the pond to the wall beside her.

"Could it be a prince?" Marci wondered. "Should I really kiss it?"

As she reached for the frog, a voice yelled, "That frog doesn't _____ to you! Put it down!"

A police officer rushed over. "What are you doing to that frog?" she asked.

"Nothing," Marci said. "I wanted to help him, _____ he might be . . ." She stopped. It sounded so silly. She got up and sadly walked away.

"Now I'll never be sure," Marci thought.

frog
long
along
off
belong
strong
water
always
mall
tall
talk
walk
bought
brought
draw
because

Subjects and Predicates

The subject of a sentence tells who or what is doing the action or is being talked about.

(Sally) danced.
(The cat) jumped off the chair.

The predicate of a sentence tells what the subject does or did.

Sally _danced_.
The cat _jumped off the chair_.

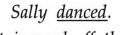 Unscramble the spelling words as you write each sentence below. Then circle the subject and underline the predicate.

1. Jack dived into the ratwe.

2. My sister hid behind a latl tree.

3. Harry tughob a baseball.

4. Marcia owns that toy gofr.

5. Mrs. Martin took a nogl vacation.

6. A orntgs wind blew across the lake.

7. I will wrad a picture of you.

8. The old clock fell fof the shelf.

AFTER THE TEST . . .

1. Did you spell all the words on your test correctly? _____

   If you did, go on to WRITE NOW! If you missed a word, it is important to know why.

2. Did you forget the letter <u>l</u> in <u>talk</u> or <u>walk</u>? _____

3. Did you put in an extra letter?

   _____

4. Did you put letters in the wrong order in <u>because</u>? _____

5. If you made some other mistake, what was it? _____

6. Write the words you missed.

   _____

   _____

NOW WHAT ?

It helps some people to hear a word spelled in a special way. If you have trouble with some spelling words, it may be fun for you to try this.

Spell the word out loud. But start with a low voice and get higher with each letter. Do this until you think you can spell the word.

WRITE NOW!

Here are four more words with /ô/:
dogs   talking   walked   cost
Use three of these words in a story about a talking dog. You might begin: It was strange that he never barked when he was a puppy.

Lesson 33 Words with /ou/

Listen for /ou/ as you say each word.

hour

sound

ground

about

house

around

count

our

found

owl

down

power

brown

tower

town

flower

1. Write two words that sound exactly the same but are not spelled the same.

_____

2. Write three words that end with the last three letters of <u>clown</u>.

_____

3. Which word ends with /s/? _____

4. Write two words that end with the letter <u>t</u>.

_____

5. Write two words that begin with the vowel <u>o</u>.

_____

6. Which three words end with the letters <u>er</u>?

_____

_____

7. Write four words that have the last four letters of <u>round</u>.

_____

_____

8. Write the two words in which you see the letter <u>a</u> but don't hear /ă/ or /ā/.

_____

Checkpoint

Write a spelling word for each clue.
Then use the Checkpoint Study Plan on page 224.

1. You tell time with a second, a minute, and an ___.

2. Another word for almost and nearly is ___.

3. Another word for land and earth is ___.

4. A very tall part of a building is a ___.

5. A bird that says "Whooo?" is an ___.

6. If you're going in a circle, you're going ___.

7. Your home is your ___.

8. Part of a plant with petals is a ___.

9. Something you hear is a ___.

10. The opposite of up is ___.

11. The opposite of lost is ___.

12. The color of chocolate is ___.

13. Will you come to ___ party?

14. Another word for strength is ___.

15. To say numbers in order is to ___.

16. Long ago, people built fences and walls around cities. These fences and walls protected the people from enemies and thieves. In the Old English language, a fence or wall was called a *toun*. Soon, a fence or wall became a sign that people lived nearby. So a place where people lived became known as a *toun*. That is what the mystery word means today. Can you guess it? ___

Use each word once to complete this story.

THE OWL

Of all the birds, owls are _____ the easiest to recognize. They all have large, round heads. They have big eyes that look straight ahead.

Owls come in several colors. Snowy owls are white. Owls of the deep rain forest are often dark _____ in color.

At last _____ , there were 132 different kinds of owls. Scientists think some owls are in danger of becoming extinct. They feel it is

_____ duty to protect the owl. Owls are not only beautiful. They are also useful to people. Owls help farmers. They eat rodents that hurt the crops.

Owls can be _____ almost every place in the world. An _____ will make its home in a tree or in a barn. Some owls will even nest on top of a water _____ near a busy _____.

Most owls hunt for food at night. The owls' eyes are very large, so they see well in the dark. Owls also have very good hearing. With their sharp hearing and keen sight, they fly above the _____ looking for small animals, such as mice and rats. Owls are meat eaters. They will never eat a plant or a _____. An owl can swoop _____ without making a _____. Once caught, an animal has little chance of getting away from the _____ of the owl's grip. In one _____ an owl can catch two or three mice.

Owls are as good at catching mice as cats are. But owls do not make good _____ pets. Owls need room to fly _____.

hour
sound
ground
about
house
around
count
our
found
owl
down
power
brown
tower
town
flower

179

Review of Capitals

Use a capital letter to begin:

- *the first word of a sentence* • *the word I*
- *the names of people and pets* • *the names of cities and states*
- *the names of streets*

★ Write each sentence. Put capital letters where they belong.

1. todd lives in lexington.

2. his friend, graham, lives around the corner.

3. every saturday, they get together.

4. graham and todd spend hours exploring.

5. they always take brown bags full of snacks.

6. saturday, at tower avenue, they heard a sound.

7. graham's dog, rovereena, had found them.

8. "you can always count on rovereena to try to get into the act!"

said graham.

Wrap Up

LESSON 33

AFTER THE TEST . . .

1. Did you spell all the words on

   your test correctly? _____

   If you did, go on to WRITE NOW! If you missed a word, it is important to know why.

2. Did you leave out a letter?

   _____

3. Did you write <u>hour</u> instead of

   <u>our</u>? _____

4. Did you forget <u>er</u> at the end of <u>power</u>, <u>flower</u>, or <u>tower</u>?

   _____

5. If you made some other mistake,

   what was it? _____

6. Write the words you missed.

   _____

WRITE NOW!

Here are four more words with /ou/:

cloud   out   now   crown

Use three of these words to write a story about someone who lived alone in the sky.

NOW WHAT ?

It helps some people to see a word in writing. If you have trouble with some spelling words, it may be fun for you to try this.

Write the word as many times as you need to. But don't lift your pencil off the paper. Say each letter as you write it. Then close your eyes and spell the word three times in a row. Ask a friend to listen to make sure you spell it correctly.

181

Lesson 34 /î/, /â/, and /ī/

Listen for /î/ or /â/ or /ī/ as you say each word.

hear

dear

ear

near

year

here

deer

★

stairs

air

chair

hair

care

where

★

tire

fire

wire

1. Write two words that begin with the letter <u>d</u> and sound exactly alike but are spelled differently.

2. Write two words that begin with the letter <u>h</u> and sound exactly alike but are spelled differently.

3. Write three words that end with the last three letters of <u>hire</u>.

4. Write the word that begins with /hw/.

5. Which four words have the letters <u>air</u>?

6. Write the word that starts with /k/.

7. Write five words that have the letters <u>ear</u>.

8. Write the word that sounds exactly like <u>hare</u>.

Checkpoint

Write a spelling word for each clue.
Then use the Checkpoint Study Plan on page 224.

1. You hear with an ___.

2. It takes 365 days to make one ___.

3. You drink water, and you breathe ___.

4. To go up to the next floor, you climb the ___.

5. An animal that lives in the forest is a ___.

6. When something burns it is on ___.

7. Don't trip over the telephone ___.

8. Something that grows on your head is ___.

9. Begin a letter with the word ___.

10. If you worry about someone, you ___.

11. When you listen, you ___.

12. The opposite of far is ___.

13. The opposite of there is ___.

14. You ask when, what, why, and ___.

15. Dad changed the flat ___.

16. Have you ever played the telephone game? One person whispers something to another person who whispers it to another, and so on. Often, the last person hears a very different message. This mystery word started as the Greek word *cathedra*. *Cathedra* meant seat. The French changed it to *chaiere*. The English changed it, too. Can you guess it? ___

183

Use each word once to complete this poem.

A Strange Story

Come sit _____ me, _____ children.

Come sit right over _____ .

I have a little story,

I tell just once a _____ .

Put a big log on the _____ .

Come close to my little _____ .

And you will hear a story

That's going to curl your _____ .

Take _____ to listen closely.

Let me have your _____ .

This is the strangest story

That you may ever _____ !

I was on my way to go to bed.

I was halfway up the stairs,

When a herd of _____ came running down

With fourteen polar bears!

Before I could catch a breath of _____ ,

Before I could go one step higher,

What do you think went rolling past?

A big, round, tow truck _____ .

(A monkey tried to lasso it

With a lasso made of _____ !)

How did those animals get there?

_____ did those animals go?

I've asked myself a hundred times,

But still I do not know!

Some nights when it's time to go to bed,

And I start to climb the _____ ,

I think I hear the echo

Of deer and polar bears!

hear
dear
ear
near
year
here
deer
stairs
air
chair
hair
care
where
tire
fire
wire

Dictionary Review

The pronunciation key of a dictionary uses letters and symbols to show how words are pronounced. Look at the pronunciation key on page 196 of the Spelling Dictionary.

★ Below are three sounds from the pronunciation key. Match each of these words with a sound from the pronunciation key.

stairs   fire   high   year   where   tire   here   hair   near

1. â as in <u>care</u> _____   _____   _____

2. ī as in <u>pie</u> _____   _____   _____

3. î as in <u>fierce</u> _____   _____   _____

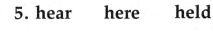

★ Look at the third letter of each word. Then write the words in each group in alphabetical order.

4. **deer   deck   dear**   5. **hear   here   held**

_____   _____

_____   _____

_____   _____

★ Write these words in alphabetical order. Use first, second, and third letters.

6. **you   where   year   which**   7. **care   wire   air   chair**

_____   _____

_____   _____

_____   _____

_____   _____

Here are the ways /î/ is spelled in this lesson: **ea, e, ee.** Here are the ways /â/ is spelled in this lesson: **ai, a, e.**

Here is the way /ī/ is spelled in this lesson: **i_e.**

LESSON 34

AFTER THE TEST...

1. Did you spell all the words on your test correctly? _____
If you did, go on to WRITE NOW! If you missed a word, it is important to know why.

2. Did you put letters in the wrong order? _____

3. Did you put in an extra letter?
_____

4. Did you write <u>dear</u> instead of <u>deer</u>, or <u>hear</u> instead of <u>here</u>?
_____

5. If you made some other mistake, what was it? _____

6. Write the words you missed.
_____
_____

NOW WHAT ?

It helps some people to hear and see a word spelled. If you have trouble with some spelling words, it may be fun for you to try this.

Go where you can be alone. Write a word in small letters. Whisper each letter as you write it. Then write the word in bigger letters. Say each letter in a medium voice as you write it. Then write the word in very big letters. Shout each letter as you write it. Do this until you can spell the word.

WRITE NOW!

Here are four more words with /â/ or /î/:

nearly pair bear pear

Use two of these words to write a

rhyme about an animal that lived in the woods. For example:

I saw a bear.
She ate a pear.

Lesson 35 Adding er and est

Say each word.

stronger

strongest

taller

tallest

greater

greatest

longer

longest

sharper

sharpest

funnier

funniest

dirtier

dirtiest

hotter

hottest

Complete the word equations.

1. tall   +   er   = _____

2. long   +   er   = _____

3. great   +   er   = _____

4. sharp   +   er   = _____

5. strong   +   er   = _____

6. tall   +   est   = _____

7. long   +   est   = _____

8. great   +   est   = _____

9. sharp   +   est   = _____

10. strong   +   est   = _____

11. dirty   − y + i   + er   = _____

12. funny   − y + i   + er   = _____

13. dirty   − y + i   + est = _____

14. funny   − y + i   + est = _____

15. hot   + t + er   = _____

16. hot   + t + est = _____

Checkpoint

Write a spelling word for each clue.
Then use the Checkpoint Study Plan on page 224.

1. If I am shorter than you, you are ____.

2. If John is taller than both of us, he is the ____.

3. The pencil with the pointiest point is the ____.

4. The silliest joke is the ____.

5. The one that has more strength is ____.

6. Pull the taffy to make it ____ .

7. The one that is the most wonderful is the ____.

8. The opposite of weakest is ____.

9. The opposite of sadder is ____.

10. The opposite of colder is ____.

11. The opposite of coldest is ____.

12. You say long, longer, ____.

13. You say great, ____ , greatest.

14. The opposite of duller is ____.

15. This mystery word means "not clean." It used to be spelled *dritti*. But people began to change its spelling. They made the first <u>i</u> change places with the <u>r</u>. Then they changed the final <u>i</u> to <u>y</u>. However, when <u>er</u> or <u>est</u> are added to the word, the <u>y</u> turns back to <u>i</u>. If you add <u>er</u> to the mystery word, you get ____.

16. Add <u>est</u> to the mystery word and get ____.

Big Splash

Use each word once to complete this story.

Ali, Sue, and Ted were playing in the park. Ali said, "Wow, it's hot for spring !"

Ted wiped his face and said, "It's

_____ than it's been all month."

"It's the _____ it's ever been,"

cried Sue. She gave a sharp whistle. Ali gave an

even _____ one. But both girls had

to cover their ears. Ted's whistle was the

_____ of all.

"Oh, Ted. You think you're so great," said Sue.

"You think you're _____ than

anyone," cried Ali.

"Well, my whistle was the _____,"

boasted Ted. "But I'll show you. Let's have a real

contest. Let's play tug of war."

Each one wanted to win. Sue was strong.

But Ted thought he was _____

than Sue. And Ali thought she was the

_____.

You don't have to be tall to be strong. Ali wasn't very tall. Sue was _____ than she was. And Ted was the _____.

"Let's put this mud puddle between us," said Ted. "The loser will fall and get dirty."

"I bet you'll get _____ than I will," said Sue.

"You'll be the _____ of all," cried Ali.

Ted and Sue were first. They pulled the rope for a long time. Sue and Ali were next. They pulled for an even _____ time. Ted and Ali were last. Their contest was the _____.

Finally, Ali pulled Ted into the mud. He fell with a big splash. The mud flew. There were big spots on Ali's face. Sue had mud on her sweater.

"You may be the winner, Ali, but you sure look funny," said Sue.

"No _____ than you," said Ali.

Ted just sat in the puddle. "I must look the _____ of all!" he laughed.

191

stronger
strongest
taller
tallest
greater
greatest
longer
longest
sharper
sharpest
funnier
funniest
dirtier
dirtiest
hotter
hottest

Adjectives

An adjective describes a noun or pronoun by telling what kind, how many, or which one.

> The <u>strong</u> man lifted the box.
> Mike is <u>strong</u>.

Add <u>er</u> to many adjectives to compare two people or things.

> Cliff is <u>stronger</u> than Mike.

Add <u>est</u> to many adjectives to compare more than two people or things.

> Paul is the <u>strongest</u> of all.

★ Write the sentences below. Use these words to fill in the blanks.

greater   hotter   funniest   tallest

1. Sharon tells the ___ jokes we've heard.

_____

_____

2. The sun is ___ today than it was yesterday.

_____

_____

3. Gilly is the ___ girl on the basketball team.

_____

_____

4. Twenty is ___ than ten.

Wrap Up ★★★

LESSON 35

AFTER THE TEST...

1. Did you spell all the words on your test correctly? _____
If you did, go on to WRITE NOW! If you missed a word, it is important to know why.

2. Did you forget to change <u>y</u> to <u>i</u> before adding <u>er</u> or <u>est</u>? _____

3. Did you forget to double the final <u>t</u> in <u>hot</u> before adding <u>er</u> or <u>est</u>? _____

4. Did you put letters in the wrong order? _____

5. If you made some other mistake, what was it? _____

6. Write the words you missed.

_____

_____

NOW WHAT ?

Some people learn best by hearing a word spelled. If you have trouble with some words, it may be fun for you to try this.

Look at the word. Spell it out loud. Do this until you know how to spell the word. Then spell the word for a friend.

WRITE NOW!

Here are four more words with <u>er</u> or <u>est</u>:

prettier prettiest fewer fewest

Use two of these words to write an ad for a flower shop that is having a sale on roses.

Lesson 36 Words in Review

A. corner

floor

pour

quart

B. strong

bought

because

talk

C. count

tower

D. near

here

deer

stairs

where

wire

★ Use a piece of paper for the starred activities.

1. In Lesson 31 you studied five ways to spell /ô/: **au, o, oo, ou, a.** Write the words in list A, which show four of these spellings.

_____

_____

2. In Lesson 32 you studied five ways to spell /ô/: **o, a, ou, aw, au.** Write the words in list B, which show four of these spellings.

_____

_____

★ 3. Write a sentence for each word in lists A and B.

4. In Lesson 33 you studied two ways to spell /ou/: **ou, ow.** Write the words in list C.

_____

5. In Lesson 34 you studied three ways to spell /î/: **ea, e, ee.** You studied three ways to spell /â/: **ai, a, e.** And you studied one way to spell /ī/: **i_e.** Write the words in list D, which show some of these spellings.

_____

_____

★ 6. Now write the review words in lists C and D. Look up each word in the Spelling Dictionary and write the sound spelling next to each word.

194

Proof It Yourself

The sentences below have been proofread. The proofreading marks tell you what mistakes have to be corrected.

- *sp* means that the word is misspelled.
- = means that a letter should be a capital.

my favorite time of year is (autumm).

My favorite time of year is autumn.

Write the sentences correctly. Use each sentence to begin a paragraph. Write each paragraph on another paper. Proofread your work.

1. My dog jinx once ate a whole (qwort) of ice cream.

_____

_____

2. i hope ann visits, (becuz) i bought her a present in Vermont.

_____

_____

3. what colors will mr. north use to paint his (howce) this time?

_____

_____

4. tim and i know a great place (ware) we can practice skating.

_____

_____

5. august is usually the (hotist) month, but it wasn't this year.

_____

_____

SPELLING
Dic·tion·ar·y

Pronunciation Key

/ă/	pat	/ŏ/	pot	/û/	fur
/ā/	pay	/ō/	go	/th/	the
/â/	care	/ô/	paw, for	/th/	thin
/ä/	father	/oi/	oil	/hw/	which
/ĕ/	pet	/ŏŏ/	book	/zh/	vision
/ē/	be	/ōō/	boot	/ə/	ago, item,
/ĭ/	pit	/yōō/	abuse		pencil, atom,
/ī/	pie	/ou/	out		circus
/î/	fierce	/ŭ/	cut	/ər/	butter

able | air

A

a·ble | ā′bəl | —*adjective* **abler, ablest**
Having enough skill to do something;
capable: *Arnold, the circus elephant, is
able to stand on his head.*

a·bout | ə bout′ | —*preposition* Of;
concerning: *Do you know the story about
Goldilocks and the three bears? —adverb*
Almost; nearly: *This recipe makes about
16 brownies.*

add | ăd | —*verb* **added, adding** To find
the sum of: *When you add 2 and 6, the
sum is 8.*

ad·dress | ə drĕs′ | or | ăd′ res′ |
—*noun, plural* **addresses** The place
where a person lives or receives mail:
*I want to mail a birthday card to Tom,
but I don't know his address.*

a·fraid | ə frād′ | —*adjective* Frightened;
full of fear: *I'm not afraid of the dark.*

af·ter | ăf′tər | or | äf′tər | —*preposition*
Following; at a later time than: *Mom
said I could go to Pete's after dinner.*

a·gain | ə gĕn′ | —*adverb* Once more;
another time: *It's time for a spelling test
again.*

a·go | ə gō′ | —*adjective* Past; before the
time it is now: *The bus left five minutes
ago.*

aid | ād | —*verb* **aided, aiding** To help or
assist: *Carla will aid you in finding your
new school.*

aim | ām | —*verb* **aimed, aiming** **1.** To
point at something: *Aim the dart and
then throw it at the target.* **2.** To have
a goal or a purpose: *Judy and Shari aim
to please their baseball coach.*

air | âr | —*noun* **1.** The mixture of gases
surrounding the earth: *I opened the
window to let in some air.* **2.** The
space above the earth: *The air was full
of brightly colored kites.*

a·like | ə līk′ | —*adjective* Similar; like one another: *The goldfish in my fish tank all look alike.*

al·most | ôl′mōst′ | *or* | ôl mōst′ | —*adverb* Nearly: *It is almost time for lunch.*

a·lone | ə lōn′ | —*adjective* By oneself: *I like to walk by the sea all alone.*

a·long | ə lông′ | *or* | ə lŏng′ | —*preposition* Beside the length of: *We walked along the beach.* —*adverb* Together; with someone: *When Jeff goes for a walk, his dog goes along.*

al·ways | ôl′wāz | *or* | ôl′wēz | —*adverb* At all times; every time: *Mellie always reads before she goes to bed.*

an·y·one | ĕn′ē wŭn′ | *or* | ĕn′ē wən | —*pronoun* Any person: *Has anyone in this class been to the Grand Canyon?*

ap·ple | ăp′əl | —*noun, plural* **apples** A round fruit that is red, yellow, or green: *My favorite type of fruit pie is apple.*

A·pril | ā′prəl | —*noun* The fourth month of the year: *I play jokes on my brother every April Fool's Day.*

aren't | ärnt | *or* | är′ənt | The contraction of "are not": *Why aren't you coming to the playground with us?*

arm | ärm | —*noun, plural* **arms** The part of the body between the hand and the shoulder: *Zelda's arm hurt from pitching.*

a·round | ə round′ | —*adverb* In a circle: *I watched the robin fly around.* —*preposition* About; here and there: *The circus traveled around the country.*

art | ärt | —*noun, plural* **arts** **1.** A painting, drawing, or sculpture. **2.** A skill or craft: *Dancing is an art.*

ask | ăsk | *or* | äsk | —*verb* **asked, asking** **1.** To put a question to: *I asked my father where he was born.* **2.** To request: *I asked for a small pizza.*

ate | āt | Look up **eat.** • **Ate** sounds like **eight.**

Au·gust | ô′gəst | —*noun* The eighth month of the year: *The weather is always so hot in August.*

au·tumn | ô′təm | —*noun, plural* **autumns** The season of the year coming between summer and winter; fall: *Every autumn the leaves change color and then fall off the trees.*

a·way | ə wā′ | —*adverb* **1.** In a different direction or place: *James steered his kite away from all the other kites.* **2.** From a place: *Take these dogs away.*

B

bark[1] | bärk | —*noun, plural* **barks** The sharp, explosive sound made by a dog or fox: *I could hear my dog's bark a mile away.* —*verb* To make the sharp sound a dog makes: *Fido likes to bark at cats.*

bark[2] | bärk | —*noun, plural* **barks** The outer covering of trees and other woody plants: *The bark of a birch tree is thin and peels off easily.*

barn | bärn | —*noun, plural* **barns** A farm building used for storing grain and hay and for keeping livestock: *The farmer checked to see if his cows were in the barn.*

be | bē | —*helping* or *auxiliary verb* **was** | wŏz | *or* | wŭz | *or* | wəz |, **were** | wûr |, **been** | bĭn | Be is used as a helping verb with action words to show continuing action: *I **was** running as fast as I could, but Ida was winning. When will you **be** finished with the crayons? We **were** about to leave, when the telephone rang. Timmy has **been** gone for over two hours.*

bear | bâr | —*noun, plural* **bears** A large animal with long, shaggy hair and a short tail: *The bear stood up on its hind legs.* • **Bear** sounds like **bare.**

be·came | bĭ kām′ | Look up **become.**

be·cause | bĭ kôz′ | *or* | bĭ kŭz′ | —*conjunction* Since; for the reason that: *The class laughed because the cartoons were so silly.*

be·come | bĭ kŭm′ | —*verb* **became** | bĭ kām′ |, **become, becoming** To come or grow to be: *The firefighter became a hero when he saved a boy.*

been | bĭn | Look up **be.**

be·fore | bĭ fôr′ | *or* | bĭ fōr′ | —*conjunction* Earlier than; ahead of: *Steve always practiced the violin before he went to soccer practice.*

be·gin | bĭ gĭn′ | —*verb* **began, begun, beginning** | bĭ gĭn′ĭng | To start: *The teams were ready to begin the game. It was beginning to rain.*

be·gin·ning | bĭ gĭn′ĭng | —*noun, plural* **beginnings** The first part: *At the beginning of the race, Todd was ahead.*

be·hind | bĭ hīnd′ | —*preposition* **1.** Following: *Joe and Al were walking behind Jeff.* **2.** At the back of: *Maria hid behind a tree.*

be·long | bĭ lông′ | *or* | bĭ lŏng′ | —*verb* **belonged, belonging** To be owned by: *Who does this dog belong to?*

best | bĕst | —*adjective* Most excellent, finest: *It was the best ice cream she had ever eaten.*

bet·ter | bĕt′ər | —*adjective* More excellent than another: *Our band played better than any other school band.*

bird | bûrd | —*noun, plural* **birds** An animal with wings and feathers that lays eggs: *A cardinal is a bird with bright red feathers.*

black | blăk | —*noun* The darkest color; the color of coal: *Black is the color of crows.* —*adjective* **blacker, blackest,** Having this color: *My dog is all white except for a black patch.*

block | blŏk | —*noun, plural* **blocks** Part of a city, often a square, with streets on all sides: *The kids that live on my block have formed a softball team.* —*verb* **blocked, blocking** To get in the way of: *The cow blocked the railroad track.*

blow | blō | —*verb* **blew, blown, blowing** To be in motion, as the air: *Hold onto your hat or the wind will blow it away.*

blue | bloo | —*adjective* **bluer, bluest** Having the color of the clear sky during the day: *Hal wore a blue jacket.* • **Blue** sounds like **blew.**

boat | bōt | —*noun, plural* **boats** A vessel that travels on water: *My sister and I went for a ride on the boat.*

bod·y | bŏd′ē | —*noun, plural* **bodies** All of a person or animal except the mind: *The quills on a porcupine's body protect it from other animals.*

boil | boil | —*verb* **boiled, boiling** To heat a liquid until bubbles form and steam is given off: *I boiled some water to make soup.*

book | book | —*noun, plural* **books** Sheets of paper with printing held together with a cover: *Richie went to the library to get a book.*

born | bôrn | *or* | bōrn | —*verb* Brought into life: *George Washington was born on February 22, 1732.*

both | bōth | —*pronoun* The one as well as the other: *Both my sisters can play the French horn.*

bot·tle | bŏt′l | —*noun, plural* **bottles** A hollow container made of glass or plastic that can be closed with a cap:

The children were so thirsty that they drank the juice from the bottles.

bot·tom | bŏt′əm | —*noun, plural* **bottoms** The lowest part of anything: *From the top of the hill I could barely see my brother down at the bottom.*

bought | bôt | Look up **buy.**

boy | boi | —*noun, plural* **boys** A male child: *My dog chased the boy on the bike.*

break | brāk | —*verb* **broke, broken, breaking** 1. To crack or damage; to come apart: *Did you break the dish when you dropped it?* 2. To crack the bone of: *Lucy fell off her bike and broke her arm.*

bright | brīt | —*adjective* **brighter, brightest** Giving off light; shining: *The bright sun made me blink.*

bring | brĭng | —*verb* **brought** | brôt |, **bringing** To carry or take something to a place or person: *He brought his photo album to school.*

broil | broil | —*verb* **broiled, broiling** To cook by holding directly over or under heat: *Jane broiled the steaks for dinner.*

brought | brôt | Look up **bring.**

brown | broun | —*adjective* **browner, brownest** Having the color of coffee or chocolate: *The dead leaves were brown.*

build | bĭld | —*verb* **built, building** To make something by putting materials or parts together: *Many birds build nests in the spring.*

bus·y | bĭz′ē | —*adjective* **busier, busiest** At work; active: *She is busy doing her homework.*

but·ter | bŭt′ər | —*noun* A soft yellow fat made from cream: *Ann spread butter on her corn on the cob.*

buy | bī | —*verb* **bought** | bôt |, **buying** To get by paying a price: *He bought a*

rocket model at the hobby shop. I'll buy popcorn at the hockey game. • **Buy** sounds like **by.**

by | bī | —*preposition* Beside or near to: *Leave your boots by the door.* • **By** sounds like **buy.**

C

cake | kāk | —*noun, plural* **cakes** A mixture of flour, milk, sugar, eggs, etc., that is baked and often covered with icing: *Mom baked two cakes for my party.*

came | kām | Look up **come.**

can | kăn | *or* | kən | —*helping or auxiliary verb* Past tense **could** | kŏod | *or* | kəd | To be able to: *We could walk to the store if you're not too tired.*

can·not | kăn′ŏt′ | *or* | kă nŏt′ | *or* | kə nŏt′ | The negative form of the verb **can.** Unable to: *You cannot blow a bubble as big as mine.*

can't | kănt | *or* | känt | The contraction of "cannot": *I can't stand wet feet.*

car | kär | —*noun, plural* **cars** An automobile: *The parking lot was full of cars.*

card | kärd | —*noun, plural* **cards** A small rectangular piece of cardboard or plastic: *Pen pals get cards from all over the world.*

care | kâr | —*noun, plural* **cares** Close attention: *The painter picked her colors with a lot of care.* —*verb* **cared, caring** To be concerned: *Millie cared what people thought about her.*

car·ry | kăr′ē | —*verb* **carried, carrying, carries** To take from one place to another: *Will you help me carry these groceries home?*

catch | kăch | —*verb* **caught, catching**
   1. To get hold of; capture: *Billy tried to catch the cat.* **2.** To reach or get to in time: *I had to hurry to catch the train.*

cent | sĕnt | —*noun, plural* **cents** A coin that is ¹/₁₀₀ of a dollar; a penny: *Bobby bought the notebook for 99 cents.* • **Cent** sounds like **sent.**

chair | châr | —*noun, plural* **chairs** A seat for one person, usually having four legs and a back: *The chair was so soft and comfortable, Jocy fell asleep.*

change | chānj | —*verb* **changed, changing** **1.** To make different: *Leaves change color in the fall.* **2.** To replace; exchange: *I'll change this dress for a different one.* —*noun, plural* **changes** A thing that has become different: *The change in your homework is very good.*

chest | chĕst | —*noun, plural* **chests** **1.** A large box with a lid: *The pirates hid a chest of gold.* **2.** The upper front of the body, enclosed by the ribs and containing the heart and lungs: *I have a cold in my chest.*

child | chīld | —*noun, plural* **children** | chĭl′drən | A young boy or girl: *Every child in the school went on the picnic. All children like fairy tales.*

chil·dren | chĭl′drən | Look up **child.**

choice | chois | —*noun, plural* **choices** The power or chance to choose: *They had their choice of peanut butter sandwiches or tuna salad for lunch.*

cir·cus | sûr′kəs | —*noun, plural* **circuses** A traveling show of performers, wild animals, and clowns: *I love to watch the clowns in the circus.*

cit·y | sĭt′ē | —*noun, plural* **cities** A large or important town: *Mom goes to the city every day to work.*

class | klăs | *or* | kläs | —*noun, plural* **classes** A group of students taught by the same teacher or group of teachers: *Our class took a trip to the museum.*

clock | klŏk | —*noun, plural* **clocks** An instrument that tells time: *According to the kitchen clock, I was late again.*

close | klōs | —*adjective* **closer, closest** Near: *Sam is standing close to the door.* —*verb* | klōz | **closed, closing** To

shut: *The suitcase was too full to close. I put the cookies in the oven and closed the door.*

cloud | kloud | —*noun, plural* **clouds** A large white mass made up of tiny drops of water floating in the sky: *I watched the airplane fly into the cloud.*

clown | kloun | —*noun, plural* **clowns** A person who has a job in the circus or on stage making people laugh: *The clowns had big shoes and rubber noses.*

coast | kōst | —*noun, plural* **coasts** The part of land that touches the sea: *Parts of the Atlantic coast are very rocky.*

coat | kōt | —*noun, plural* **coats** A piece of clothing worn over other clothes to keep warm: *Laura's new coat had a hood and a big zipper.*

co·coa | kō′kō′ | —*noun* A sweet drink made with cocoa and milk or water: *The best thing about ice-skating is drinking hot cocoa afterward.*

coin | koin | —*noun, plural* **coins** A piece of round, flat metal stamped by the government, used for money: *I had a lot of coins in my pocket.*

col·or | kŭl′ər | —*noun, plural* **colors** Red, yellow, blue, or any combination of these: *Sally's dress was the color of sunshine.* —*verb* **colored, coloring** To give color to: *Betty drew an elephant and colored it pink.*

comb | kōm | —*noun, plural* **combs** A thin piece of hard material with teeth, used to arrange hair: *While Alice was untangling her hair, the comb broke.* —*verb* **combed, combing** **1.** To arrange the hair: *I comb my dog's hair every day.* **2.** To look thoroughly: *We combed the house for the missing watch.*

come | kŭm | —*verb* **came** | kām |, **coming** **1.** To draw near; approach: *The lion came closer and closer to the mouse.* **2.** To be available: *The toy robot came with two batteries.*

cook | kŏŏk | —*verb* **cooked, cooking** To prepare food for eating by using heat: *Cook the rice until it is fluffy.*

cook·y or **cook·ie** | kŏŏk′ē | —*noun, plural* **cookies** A small, flat, sweet cake: *The cookies were shaped like hearts.*

cool | kōōl | —*adjective* **cooler, coolest** Not warm; slightly cold: *The cool breeze made me shiver.*

cor·ner | kôr′nər | —*noun, plural* **corners** The place where two lines or sides meet: *My dog ate a corner of my homework paper.*

cost | kôst | —*noun, plural* **costs** The price of something: *The cost of everything is going up!* —*verb* **cost, costing** To have as a price: *How much do these shoes cost?*

could | kŏŏd | *or* | kəd | Look up **can.**

couldn't | kŏŏd′nt | The contraction of "could not": *We couldn't go to the beach because it was raining.*

count | kount | —*noun, plural* **counts** The number reached by counting: *A count showed that one marble was missing.* —*verb* **counted, counting** To say numbers in order: *Fran's baby sister can count to 20.*

cov·er | kŭv′ər | —*verb* **covered, covering** To put or lay over: *I covered my bread with peanut butter.* —*noun, plural* **covers** Something that is put over another thing: *He hid the present under the covers on his bed.*

cow·boy | kou′boi′ | —*noun, plural* **cowboys** A man who herds cattle on a ranch, usually on horseback: *The cowboy fell off his horse.*

crown | kroun | —*noun, plural* **crowns** A covering for the head worn by kings and queens, usually made of gold and jewels: *The queen wore her crown every day.* —*verb* To put a crown upon the head: *The new king was crowned in front of all his subjects.*

cry | krī | —*verb* **cried, crying, cries** **1.** To weep; shed tears: *Some people cry when they are happy.* **2.** To shout or call loudly: *If I need help, I'll cry out.*

curl | kûrl | —*verb* **curled, curling** To twist into curves or coils: *The snake curled around the rock.* —*noun, plural* **curls** A coil of hair; a ringlet: *She wore her hair in curls for the party.*

D

dan·ger | dān′jər | —*noun, plural* **dangers** The chance of something harmful happening: *A police officer faces danger every day.*

dark | därk | —*adjective* **darker, darkest** Having little or no light: *The cave was very dark inside.* —*noun* Nightfall: *The street lights come on after dark.*

dear | dîr | —*adjective* **dearer, dearest** Loved: *Billy is a dear friend of mine.* • **Dear** sounds like **deer.**

De·cem·ber | dĭ **sĕm**′bər | —*noun* The twelfth month of the year: *We are going skiing in December.*

deer | dîr | —*noun, plural* **deer** A hoofed animal that can run very fast: *Look at the beautiful antlers on that male deer.*
• **Deer** sounds like **dear.**

did·n't | **dĭd**′nt | The contraction of "did not": *I didn't know who you were.*

dime | dīm | —*noun, plural* **dimes** A United States or Canadian coin worth ten cents: *Grandma told me that ice cream cones used to cost a dime.*

dirt | dûrt | —*noun* Loose earth or soil: *He drew a map in the dirt with a stick.*

dirt·y | **dûr**′tē | —*adjective* **dirtier, dirtiest** Not clean: *I stepped in the mud and got my shoes dirty.*

dish | dĭsh | —*noun, plural* **dishes** **1.** A plate or bowl used for holding food: *The clown balanced a dish on his nose.*
2. A particular food: *Barbara's favorite dish was spaghetti.*

do | dōō | —*verb* **did, done** | dŭn |, **doing, does** | dŭz | **1.** To perform; complete: *Bibi, the circus monkey, is always doing things that make people laugh.* **2.** To be good enough: *No one had done as well on the test as Valerie.* —*helping* or *auxiliary verb* **Do** is used to ask questions: *Does she swim?*

does | dŭz | Look up **do.**

does·n't | **dŭz**′ənt | The contraction of "does not": *My little sister doesn't like to take a bath.*

dog | dôg | *or* | dŏg | —*noun, plural* **dogs** A four-footed animal related to wolves and foxes: *My dog is a white poodle.*

doing Look up **do.**

done | dŭn | Look up **do.**

don't | dōnt | The contraction of "do not": *Don't sit on that wet bench.*

door | dôr | *or* | dōr | —*noun, plural* **doors** **1.** A movable panel that swings or slides to open or close the entrance to a room, building, or vehicle: *Jill slammed the door behind her.* **2.** A doorway: *Marta walked through the door.*

down¹ | doun | —*adverb* From a higher to a lower point on: *The ball rolled down the hill.*

down² | doun | —*noun* The soft under feathers of birds: *Sandy's new ski jacket was filled with down.*

draw | drô | —*verb* **drew, drawn, drawing** To make a picture with pen, pencil, crayon, etc.: *I can draw great pictures of airplanes.*

dream | drēm | —*noun, plural* **dreams** Something felt, thought, or seen during sleep: *I had a dream about a giant bee.* —*verb* **dreamed** or **dreamt, dreaming** To think, feel, or see during sleep; have dreams: *Amy dreamed that she could fly.*

dress | drĕs | —*noun, plural* **dresses** A piece of clothing worn by women and girls, usually having a top and skirt made in one piece: *Mary bought a new dress for the class party.* —*verb* **dressed, dressing** To put clothes on: *Get dressed and we'll go shopping.*

drive | drīv | —*verb* **drove, driven, driving** **1.** To steer a vehicle: *Drive the car carefully.* **2.** To carry in a vehicle: *My mom promised to drive me to the rodeo.* —*noun, plural* **drives** A ride in a vehicle: *Let's go for a drive in the country.*

drop | drŏp | —*verb* **dropped, dropping** To fall or let fall: *The pan was so hot, he dropped it. The soap was so slippery, Barbara kept dropping it.*

E

each | ēch | —*adjective* Every one of: *Each student in the class gave a report.*

ear | îr | —*noun, plural* **ears** **1.** The part of the body with which animals and people hear: *An elephant's ears are big and floppy.* **2.** Attention: *This message is important so give me your ear.*

earth | ûrth | —*noun* **1.** The planet on which human beings live: *The Earth is the third planet from the sun.* **2.** Soil; ground: *We planted a tree in the earth.*

easy | ē′zē | —*adjective* **easier, easiest** Not hard: *The puzzle was so easy, she finished it in a minute.*

eat | ēt | —*verb* **ate** | āt |, **eaten, eating** To take meals: *I ate dinner at my best friend's house.*

egg | ĕg | —*noun, plural* **eggs** The contents of a chicken egg, used as food: *I like to crack the shells of eggs.*

eight | āt | —*adjective* Being one more than seven in number: *An octopus has eight tentacles.* • **Eight** sounds like **ate.**

end | ĕnd | —*noun, plural* **ends** The finish of a thing: *The road comes to an end at the river* —*verb* **ended, ending** To finish; to bring to an end: *The concert ended with a fireworks show.*

end·ing | ĕn′dĭng | —*noun, plural* **endings** The last part: *The movie had a scary ending, so I closed my eyes.*

en·joy | ĕn joi′ | —*verb* **enjoyed, enjoying** To like to do: *I enjoy singing along with the radio.*

e·ven | ē′vən | —*adjective* Smooth; flat: *Willy likes to ride his bike on this road because it's so even.* —*adverb* **1.** As well as: *The boys were all dressed up, even Mitch.* **2.** In spite of: *I'll go*

horseback riding with you even though I don't like horses.

eve·ning | ēv′nĭng | —*noun, plural* **evenings** Time of day between sunset and midnight: *My family likes to sit in front of a fire on cold evenings.*

eve·ry | ĕv′rē | —*adjective* All in an entire group; each one: *Lou read every mystery book in the library.*

eve·ry·one | ĕv′rē wŭn′ | —*pronoun* Each person: *Everyone who was asked is coming to the party.*

eve·ry·thing | ĕv′rē thĭng′ | —*pronoun* All things: *Everything you need to know about dolphins is in this book.*

eye | ī | —*noun, plural* **eyes** **1.** One of two round organs with which a person or animal sees: *My eyes followed the home run right out of the field.* **2.** A close watch: *Please keep an eye on my bike.*

F

fa·ble | fā′bəl | —*noun, plural* **fables** A story that teaches a lesson: *My favorite fable is about the lion and the mouse.*

face | fās | —*noun, plural* **faces** The front of the head: *Murray had spots on his face from the measles.*

fact | făkt | —*noun, plural* **facts** Something that is true: *I know for a fact that there are no more dinosaurs.*

fam·i·ly | făm′ə lē *or* | făm′lē | —*noun, plural* **families** Parents and their children: *My family always goes on vacation together.*

fa·ther | fä′thər | —*noun, plural* **fathers** The male parent of a child: *Betty's father took her to the doctor yesterday.*

Feb·ru·ar·y | fĕb′rōō ĕr′ē | *or*
| fĕb′yōō ĕr′ē | —*noun* The second
month of the year: *Ground-Hog Day
comes in February.*

feel | fēl | —*verb* **felt, feeling** To touch
with the hand: *The horse let me feel its
silky mane.*

few | fyōō | —*adjective* **fewer, fewest** Not
many: *There were only a few peanuts
left in the bag. There are fewer cookies
here than there were a minute ago.*

fill | fĭl | —*verb* **filled, filling** **1.** To make
or become full: *I always fill the sugar
bowl to the top.* **2.** To spread
throughout: *My writing filled the pages
of my diary.*

find | fīnd | —*verb* **found** | found |,
finding **1.** To look for and get back:
I found my keys under my bed. **2.** To
look for and discover: *Polar bears are
only found in the far north.*

fine | fīn | —*adjective* **finer, finest**
Excellent; very good: *Hilary is a fine
dancer.*

fire | fīr | —*noun, plural* **fires** Heat and
light given off by burning something:
They saw the fire and ran for help.

first | fûrst | —*adjective* Coming before
any other in time, place, or order: *This
is my first pair of ice skates.* —*noun*
Person or thing that is first: *Mark was
the first in line.*
    ***Idiom.* at first.** In the beginning:
*Ellen didn't want to go swimming at
first, but she changed her mind.*

floor | flôr | *or* | flōr | —*noun, plural* **floors**
The part of a room people walk on:
The floor squeaks when you walk on it.

flow·er | flou′ər | —*noun, plural* **flowers**
The part of the plant where seeds are
made; the blossom: *This plant has
yellow flowers.*

fly | flī | —*verb* **flew, flown, flying, flies**
To move through the air with wings: *I
love to watch airplanes fly in and out of
the airport.*

foot | fŏot | —*noun, plural* **feet** The part
of the leg on which a person or animal
walks: *I put my shoe on the wrong foot.*

for·get | fər gĕt′ | —*verb* **forgot**
| fər gŏt′ |, **forgotten** To be unable to
remember: *Don't forget to study for your
math test. I forgot to study for the test.*

for·got | fər gŏt′ | Look up **forget.**

fork | fôrk | —*noun, plural* **forks** **1.** A
tool used to pick up food: *I like to eat
spaghetti with my fingers, but Mom
makes me use a fork.* **2.** A place where
something divides into more than one
part: *When we came to the fork in the
trail, we didn't know which way to go.*

found | found | Look up **find.**

four | fôr | *or* | fōr | —*noun* The number
that follows three: *Two plus two is four.*
—*adjective* Being one more than three
in number: *There are four people in my
family.*

four·teen | fôr′tēn′ | *or* | fōr′tēn′ |
—*noun* The number that follows 13:
Ten plus four is fourteen. —*adjective*
Having the number that follows 13: *My
sister has fourteen mittens.*

free | frē | —*adjective* **freer, freest**
1. Not under someone else's control:
*The cat was free to roam around the
neighborhood.* **2.** Without cost: *We
won free tickets to the show.*

Fri·day | frī′dē | *or* | frī′dā′ | —*noun,
plural* **Fridays** The sixth day of the
week: *We don't get homework on Friday.*

friend | frĕnd | —*noun, plural* **friends** A
person one knows and likes: *My friend
and I write letters to each other in a
secret code.*

frog | frôg | *or* | frŏg | —*noun, plural*
frogs A small animal with webbed feet
and smooth skin: *Frogs use their long
sticky tongues to catch insects.*

from | frŭm | *or* | frŏm | *or* | frəm |
—*preposition* **1.** Having as a place of
origin: *I got a letter from my cousin.*
2. Starting at: *The boys raced from
school to their house.*

front | frŭnt | —*noun, plural* **fronts** The
part of something that faces forward:
*There was a crowd in front of the
record store.*

full | fŏŏl | —*adjective* **fuller, fullest**
Holding all that it can hold: *My stomach
was full after dinner.*

fun·ny | fŭn′ē | —*adjective* **funnier,
funniest** Causing laughter; amusing:
*Sammy's jokes are very funny. Brad's
jokes are always funnier than mine.*

fur | fûr | —*noun, plural* **furs** Thick, soft
hair that covers certain animals: *My
dog's fur keeps him warm in the winter.*

gar·den | gär′dn | —*noun, plural* **gardens**
A piece of land used for growing
vegetables and flowers: *We planted
tomatoes and lettuce in the garden.*

get | gĕt | —*verb* **got, got** or **gotten, getting**
To gain; receive: *I am getting a new
watch next week.*

girl | gûrl | —*noun, plural* **girls** A female
child: *Barbi was the only girl on the team.*

glass | glăs | *or* | gläs | —*noun, plural*
glasses **1.** A hard, clear material used
to make windows, etc.: *Betsy hit the ball
through a window and broke the glass.*
2. A container made of glass used for
drinking: *Will you pour me a glass
of milk, please?*

go | gō | —*verb* **goes** | gōz |, **went, gone,
going** To move; travel: *Mary goes to
the dentist every week.*

goat | gōt | —*noun, plural* **goats** An
active animal about the size of a sheep,
with short horns and a beard: *Some
people eat cheese made from the milk of
a goat.*

goes | gōz | Look up **go.**

gold | gōld | —*noun* A heavy, precious,
yellow metal used for making jewelry
and coins: *James has a piece of gold
that belonged to his grandfather.*

grade | grād | —*noun, plural* **grades**
1. A class or year in school: *Sam is in
the third grade this year.* **2.** A mark
for school work: *Tina's grade on her
book report was 95.*

grape | grāp | —*noun, plural* **grapes** A
juicy fruit growing in bunches on a vine:
Dad makes jelly from grapes.

gray | grā | —*noun, plural* **grays** Any
color that is a mixture of black and
white. —*adjective* **grayer, grayest**
Having the color gray: *I have a gray cat.*

great | grāt | —*adjective* **greater, greatest**
Wonderful; very good: *It would be great
to travel around the world. This is the
greatest zoo I've ever seen.*

ground | ground | —*noun* Soil; land: *The
ground was covered with snow after the
storm.*

grow | grō | —*verb* **grew, grown, growing**
To become bigger: *The puppy is growing
more each day.*

guess | gĕs | —*verb* **guessed, guessing**
1. To form an opinion without enough
knowledge: *Let's try guessing what the
surprise will be.* **2.** To think; suppose: *I
guess I'll just stay here.*

H

had·n't | hăd′nt | The contraction of "had not": *I hadn't known him long before he moved away.*

hair | hâr | —*noun, plural* **hairs** The thin, threadlike strands that grow from a person's or animal's skin: *Nan wears her long hair in a braid.*

half | hăf | *or* | häf | —*noun, plural* **halves** One of two equal parts: *Jean ate half of her sandwich, and I ate the other half.*

ham·mer | hăm′ər | —*noun, plural* **hammers** A tool with an iron head used to drive in nails: *I need a hammer to put the birdhouse together.*

hand | hănd | —*noun, plural* **hands** The part of the arm below the wrist: *I held the baby chick in my hands.* —*verb* **handed, handing** To pass with the hands: *I handed the teacher my story.*

hap·py | hăp′ē | —*adjective* **happier, happiest** Feeling pleased or joyful: *She was happy when she won the award.*

hard | härd | —*adjective* **harder, hardest** Not easy: *This math test is too hard.* —*adverb* **harder, hardest** With energy or effort: *Biff worked hard.*

has·n't | hăz′ənt | The contraction of "has not": *Joey hasn't gone yet.*

have·n't | hăv′ənt | The contraction of "have not": *I haven't heard from Dolly since she went to camp.*

head | hĕd | —*noun, plural* **heads** The top part of the body that contains the brain, eyes, ears, nose, and mouth: *Jane put the hat on her head.* —*verb* **headed, heading** To go toward: *The bird headed south for the winter.*

hear | hîr | —*verb* **heard, hearing** **I.** To be aware of sound: *Do you hear a noise in the attic?* **2.** To be told: *Emily and her class were about to hear the story of Daniel Boone.* • **Hear** sounds like **here.**

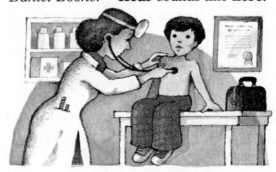

heart | härt | —*noun, plural* **hearts** **I.** The organ in the chest that pumps blood through the body: *The doctor listened to my heart.* **2.** Courage and enthusiasm: *Howard put his whole heart into winning the game.*

he'd | hēd | The contraction of "he had" or "he would": *If he'd wanted to come, he could have. He said he'd be ready in a minute.*

he'll | hēl | The contraction of "he will" or "he shall": *Larry said he'll study for the test with me later.*

hel·lo | hĕ lō′ | *or* | hə lō′ | *or* | hĕl′ō | —*interjection* A greeting: *Sharon always answers the phone with a cheery "Hello."*

help | hĕlp | —*verb* **helped, helping** To aid or assist; to be useful: *Will you help me hang this picture? I helped Dee buy new jeans.*

here | hîr | —*adverb* In this place or spot: *Cheri and I have been waiting here all afternoon.* —*noun* This place: *The ice cream truck is four blocks from here.* • **Here** sounds like **hear.**

he's | hēz | The contraction of "he is": *He's the new president of the photography club.*

high | hī | **higher, highest**—*adjective* Tall: *That pine tree is 25 feet high.* —*adverb* At or to a high point: *My balloon flew high up in the sky.*

hold | hōld | —*verb* **held, holding I.** To have and keep in the hand; grasp: *I have to hold my sister's hand when we go shopping.* **2.** To keep in a certain position: *Hold your head still while I comb your hair.*

hole | hōl | —*noun, plural* **holes** A hollow or empty place in something solid: *The pirates dug a hole and buried a treasure chest.* • **Hole** sounds like **whole.**

home | hōm | —*noun, plural* **homes** A place where a person lives: *The homes of Bart and Max are in the same apartment building.*

hood | hŏŏd | —*noun, plural* **hoods** A head covering, usually attached to a coat: *When it started to snow, I put up the hood on my coat.*

hop | hŏp | —*verb* **hopped, hopping** To move by short jumps: *The robin hopped all over the yard in search of worms.*

hope | hōp | —*verb* **hoped, hoping** To wish for something: *I hope my grandmother feels better soon. Julia hoped she wouldn't be late for school.*

horse | hôrs | —*noun, plural* **horses** A large animal with hoofs, having a mane and tail: *Spanish soldiers brought the first horses to America.*

hot | hŏt | —*adjective* **hotter, hottest** Very warm: *It is hotter outside today than it was yesterday.*

hour | our | —*noun, plural* **hours** A period of time equal to 60 minutes: *The bread will take one hour to bake.* • **Hour** sounds like **our.**

house | hous | —*noun, plural* **houses** | hou′zĭz | A building that people live in: *The scouts met at my house.*

hun·dred | hŭn′drĭd | —*noun, plural* **hundreds** The number that follows 99: *Fifty plus fifty is one hundred.* —*adjective* Being one more than 99 in number: *There are 100 pages in this book.*

hur·ry | hûr′ē | *or* | hŭr′ē | —*verb* **hurried, hurrying** To move or act quickly: *Hurry up or we'll miss the bookmobile.*

I'd | īd | The contraction of "I had," "I would," or "I should": *I'd better get home before dark. I'd rather eat brownies than bake them.*

I'll | īl | The contraction of "I will" or "I shall": *I'll never remember everyone's name.*

I'm | īm | The contraction of "I am": *I'm sure I will make the team.*

in·side | ĭn′sīd′ | *or* | ĭn sīd′ | —*noun, plural* **insides** The inner part: *We painted the inside of the house.* —*preposition* | ĭn sīd′ | Into: *She put her hand inside the grab bag and pulled out a whistle.*

is·n't | ĭz′ənt | The contraction of "is not": *This isn't my lunch box.*

it's | ĭts | The contraction of "it is" or "it has": *It's time for lunch. It's been a long time since I saw my aunt.*

I've | īv | The contraction of "I have": *I've never seen a movie that scared me as much as this one.*

Jan·u·ar·y | jăn′yŏŏ ĕr′ē | —*noun* The first month of the year: *January has 31 days.*

jog | jŏg | —*verb* **jogged, jogging** To run slowly: *My mom jogged two miles this morning.*

join | join | —*verb* **joined, joining** **1.** To put together: *We joined hands and made a circle.* **2.** To take part with others: *Will you join us for a swim across the lake?*

joke | jōk | —*noun, plural* **jokes**
Something funny said or done to make someone laugh: *Steve makes everyone laugh with his elephant jokes.* —*verb* **joked, joking** To do or say something as a joke: *I was only joking.*

joy | joi | —*noun, plural* **joys** A feeling of great happiness: *My dog jumps for joy when he sees me.*

Ju·ly | jōo lī′ | —*noun* The seventh month of the year: *Are you going on a vacation in July?*

jump | jŭmp | —*verb* **jumped, jumping** To leap: *The frog jumped from rock to rock.*

June | jōon | —*noun* The sixth month of the year: *School is over in June.*

just | jŭst | —*adjective* Fair: *Tim didn't think the teacher was just in giving a surprise test.* —*adverb* At that moment: *Just when he fell asleep the phone rang.*

K

keep | kēp | —*verb* **kept, keeping** **1.** To have; own: *You may keep the picture.* **2.** To continue in a certain condition or place; to stay: *I kept the hamster in a cage.*

key | kē | —*noun, plural* **keys** **1.** A piece of shaped metal used to open a lock: *I lost my key, so I couldn't get in the house.* **2.** The most important part: *Exercise is a key to good health.*

kick | kĭk | —*verb* **kicked, kicking** To hit with the foot: *I saw the horse kick a hole in the barn door.*

kind¹ | kīnd | —*adjective* **kinder, kindest** Thoughtful; helpful: *The nurse is a very kind person.*

kind² | kīnd | —*noun, plural* **kinds** A type; variety: *What kind of music do you like?*

knew | nōo | *or* | nyōo | Look up **know.**

know | nō | —*verb* **knew** | nōo | *or* | nyōo |, **known, knowing** **1.** To be certain of the facts: *I know you are hiding under the stairs.* **2.** To be familiar with: *Penny knew everyone in school.*

L

late | lāt | —*adverb* **later, latest** After the usual or expected time: *The school bus was waiting because I was late. John was even later today than usual.*

laugh | lăf | *or* | läf | —*verb* **laughed, laughing** To make sounds and move your face to show joy or amusement: *I couldn't help laughing at his hat.*

lay | lā | —*verb* **laid, laying** To put or place: *Roll up your sleeping bag and lay it next to mine.*

la·zy | lā′zē | —*adjective* **lazier, laziest** Unwilling to work: *John was too lazy to help his brother mow the lawn.*

lead | lēd | —*verb* **led** | lĕd |, **leading** To show the way: *The guide at the park led the way.*

learn | lûrn | —*verb* **learned** *or* **learnt, learning** To gain knowledge or skill: *Erma wants to learn how to speak Spanish.*

leave | lēv | —*verb* **left** | lĕft |, **leaving** To go away; depart: *By 8:00 A.M. I was ready to leave for school. Nellie's family left town.*

led | lĕd | Look up **lead.**

left¹ | lĕft | —*adjective* On the left side: *Tara sat on her mother's left side.*

left² | lĕft | Look up **leave.**

leg | lĕg | —*noun, plural* **legs** One of the parts of the body used for standing and walking: *Racers have strong legs.*

less | lĕs | —*adjective* Fewer: *Ten is less than a dozen.*

let·ter | lĕt'ər | —*noun, plural* **letters** A written message: *I wrote only one letter to my parents while I was at camp.*

light¹ | līt | —*noun, plural* **lights** Anything that gives off the energy by which we see, such as a lamp: *Turn off the light before you go to sleep.*

light² | līt | —*adjective* **lighter, lightest** Not heavy: *The box was light because it was empty.*

like¹ | līk | —*verb* **liked, liking** **I.** To be fond of someone or something: *I have always liked my cousin, Sal.* **2.** To enjoy: *Ida liked to dance.*

like² | līk | —*preposition.* **I.** Similar to: *Harriet's coat is just like mine.* **2.** In the mood for: *I feel like going for a walk.*

line | līn | —*noun, plural* **lines** A long row of people or things: *He stood in line for hours to get carnival tickets.*

li·on | lī'ən | —*noun, plural* **lions** A large, wild cat from Africa or Asia: *Only male lions have manes.*

list | lĭst | —*noun, plural* **lists** A series of names, numbers, or things: *I made a list of all the things I have to do today.*

lit·tle | lĭt'l | —*adjective* **littler, littlest** or **least** Small in size or quantity: *My kitten is still very little.*

live¹ | lĭv | —*verb* **lives** | lĭvz |, **lived, living** **I.** To have life; to exist: *Dinosaurs lived millions of years ago.* **2.** To make one's home; reside: *My best friend lives on a farm.*

live² | līv | —*adjective* Living: *We saw live whales at Water World.*

loaf¹ | lōf | —*noun, plural* **loaves** Bread baked in one piece or shape: *I sliced the loaf of bread that I'd just made.*

loaf² | lōf | —*verb* **loafed, loafing** To be lazy: *My dog loafs around the house.*

long | lông | *or* | lŏng | —*adjective* **longer, longest** Not short; great in length or time: *The school play was very long. That is the longest snake I have ever seen.* —*adverb* **longer, longest** For a great amount of time: *Take as long as you need to finish the test.*

look | lŏŏk | —*verb* **looked, looking** To direct the eyes to see: *Marcy looked everywhere for her necklace.* —*noun, plural* **looks** A glance: *We took a look at Fran's new piano.*

love·ly | lŭv'lē | —*adjective* **lovelier, loveliest** Beautiful: *The flowers look lovely on the table.*

low | lō | —*adjective* **lower, lowest** **I.** Not high: *The seats were so low, I couldn't see the movie.* **2.** Soft; not loud: *Keep your voice low so they won't hear us.*

lunch | lŭnch | —*noun, plural* **lunches** The midday meal: *Ethan always has a sandwich for lunch.*

M

mail | māl | —*noun* Letters or packages sent through the post office: *Did you bring in the mail today?* —*verb* **mailed, mailing** To send by mail: *I mailed a letter to the President of the United States.*

mall | môl | *or* | măl | —*noun, plural* **malls** A shopping center: *Mom took me to the mall to buy some new clothes.*

man·y | mĕn′ē | —*adjective* **more, most**
A large number of: *Many animals live in this forest.*

March | märch | —*noun* The third month of the year: *March is the best month for flying kites.*

mar·ket | mär′kĭt | —*noun, plural* **markets** A place where goods are bought and sold: *We always go to the market for fresh vegetables.*

match¹ | măch | —*verb* **matched, matching** To be alike; to look alike: *These two socks match.*

match² | măch | —*noun, plural* **matches** A small stick of wood or cardboard that bursts into flame when rubbed: *Always keep your matches in a dry place when you are camping.*

mat·ter | măt′ər | —*noun, plural* **matters** Problem or trouble: *What's the matter with your goldfish? —verb* **mattered, mattering** To be of importance: *Does it matter to you if we go to the store first?*

May | mā | —*noun* The fifth month of the year: *My family always gives a picnic on Memorial Day in May.*

meat | mēt | —*noun* The flesh of animals used as food: *We had meat and a salad for dinner.* • **Meat** sounds like **meet.**

meet | mēt | —*verb* **met, meeting** To come together; come face to face: *Meet me on the corner after school. The club is meeting this afternoon.* • **Meet** sounds like **meat.**

meet·ing | mē′tĭng | —*noun, plural* **meetings** A coming together for some common purpose: *The lion called a meeting of all the animals in his kingdom.*

mile | mīl | —*noun, plural* **miles** A unit of distance equal to 5,280 feet or 1,609.34 meters: *The baseball field is two miles away from my house.*

mind | mīnd | —*noun, plural* **minds** The part of a person that thinks, feels, learns, etc.: *He has a good mind, if only he would use it. —verb* **minded, minding** To object to: *Would you mind if I borrowed your record?*

mine | mīn | —*pronoun* The thing or things belonging to me: *That's Bobby's bed, and this one is mine.*

Mon·day | mŭn′dē | *or* | mŭn′dā′ | —*noun* The second day of the week: *Sometimes it's hard to wake up on Monday.*

mon·ey | mŭn′ē | —*noun* Coins and paper bills printed by a government and used to pay for things: *Judy is saving her money to buy a radio.*

month | mŭnth | —*noun* One of 12 parts the year is divided into: *My birthday is this month.*

morn·ing | môr′nĭng | —*noun, plural* **mornings** The early part of the day: *I have cereal for breakfast every morning.*

most | mōst | —*adjective* The greatest amount: *The team that gets the most runs will win. —noun* The larger part: *I like most of the people in this club.*

moth·er | mŭth′ər | —*noun, plural* **mothers** A female parent of a child: *Marty's mother writes articles for magazines.*

move | mōov | —*verb* **moved, moving** To change from one position to another: *Mom is always moving the furniture around. —noun, plural* **moves** The act of moving: *The frog made his move and caught the fly.*

much | mŭch | **more, most—***adjective* Great in amount: *I have much work to do. —adverb* Greatly; to a large degree: *Frank is much excited about his award.*

mu·sic | **myōo′**zĭk | —*noun* The art of combining pleasing sounds: *Becky loves to make music on the piano.*

must | mŭst | —*helping* or *auxiliary verb* Will have to; should: *You must wear a smock in art class.*

must·n't | **mŭs′**ənt | The contraction of "must not": *Carl mustn't have heard the dinner bell.*

N

near | nîr | —*adverb* **nearer, nearest** Not far from; close to: *Randy lives near his grandparents.*

near·ly | **nîr′**lē | —*adverb* Almost: *Terry had nearly enough money to buy the paint set.*

need | nēd | —*verb* **needed, needing** To require; must have: *I need a whistle to call my dog.*

nev·er | **nĕv′**ər | —*adverb* Not at any time: *Ben never gives up.*

news | nōoz | *or* | nyōoz | —*noun* (Used with a singular verb.) Recent events or information: *The news about the science fair is good.*

next | nĕkst | —*adjective* **1.** Coming right after: *We'll get on the next car of the roller coaster.* **2.** Nearest in position: *Chuck lives in the next apartment.*

nice | nīs | —*adjective* **nicer, nicest** Pleasant; agreeable: *It was a nice evening for a walk.*

night | nīt | —*noun, plural* **nights** The time between sunset and sunrise: *On a clear night, it's fun to look at the stars.*

noise | noiz | —*noun, plural* **noises** A sound, especially if loud: *The crying baby made a lot of noise.*

none | nŭn | —*pronoun* Not any; not one: *None of my friends can ski.*

noon | nōon | —*noun* Midday; 12 o'clock in the middle of the day: *Walter went home at noon for lunch.*

north | nôrth | —*noun* The direction toward the North Pole: *A compass needle always points the way north.* —*adverb* Toward the north: *Bobby walked north to go into town.*

nose | nōz | —*noun, plural* **noses** The part of the head through which people and animals breathe and smell: *My nose could smell the apple pie baking in the oven.*

noth·ing | **nŭth′**ĭng | —*pronoun* **1.** Not anything: *Nothing the clown did made the child smile.* **2.** Of no importance: *It's nothing at all.* **3.** Zero: *The score was one to nothing.*

No·vem·ber | nō **vĕm′**bər | —*noun* The eleventh month of the year: *We eat turkey in November.*

now | nou | —*adverb* At the present time; immediately: *Can you come over to my house now?*

num·ber | **nŭm′**bər | —*noun, plural* **numbers** **1.** A figure or numeral that identifies something: *His football number is 12.* **2.** Amount: *Tell me the number of marbles you have.*

O

o·bey | ō **bā′** | —*verb* **obeyed, obeying** To follow orders: *Ronnie's dog would not obey him.*

o'clock | ə **klŏk′** | —*adverb* According to the clock: *My favorite TV show begins at 7 o'clock.*

Oc·to·ber | ôk tō'bər | —*noun* The tenth month of the year: *Halloween is the last day of October.*

off | ôf | *or* | ŏf | —*adjective* Not on; removed: *He worked with his shirt off.* —*preposition* Away from a place: *She dived off the pier.*

oil | oil | —*noun* **1.** A greasy liquid or a fat that easily becomes liquid: *We dropped the popcorn into the hot oil.* **2.** Petroleum: *They drill for oil.*

once | wŭns | —*adverb* Only one time: *I'll play the song only once.*

one | wŭn | —*noun* A number, written 1: *One plus two equals three.* —*pronoun* A particular person or thing: *One of my turtles is missing.* • **One** sounds like **won.**

on·ly | ōn'lē | —*adjective* Sole; without others: *This is my only brother, Harold.* —*adverb* Just; merely: *Phil was 14, but he acted as if he were only 4.*

o·pen | ō'pən | —*verb* **opened, opening** To cause something to be no longer closed: *I couldn't wait to open the box that was for me.*

or·der | ôr'dər | —*noun, plural* **orders** **1.** A command: *The captain gave the order to sail.* **2.** An arrangement of things: *The words in the list are in alphabetical order.*

oth·er | ŭth'ər | —*adjective* Different: *I have other things to do.* —*noun, plural* **others** The remaining people or things: *Mom carried the big box and I carried all the others.*

our | our | —*pronoun* Of or belonging to us: *Our dog followed us to school.* • **Our** sounds like **hour.**

out | out | —*adverb* **1.** Not in: *The cat was out all day.* **2.** At an end: *The firefighters put out the fire.*

ov·en | ŭv'ən | —*noun, plural* **ovens** An enclosed space for baking or heating food: *I watched as they took the hot pizza from the oven.*

o·ver | ō'vər | —*preposition* **1.** Above; higher than: *It was raining, but at least we had a tent over our heads.* **2.** On top of; upon: *Teddy spilled raisins all over the floor.* —*adjective* Finished: *The play is over.*

owl | oul | —*noun, plural* **owls** A kind of bird with a flat face, large eyes, and a short, hooked beak. Owls make a hooting sound: *The hoot of the owl scares some people.*

own | ōn | —*verb* **owned, owning** To have; possess: *Do you own the dog that is following you?*

P

page¹ | pāj | —*noun, plural* **pages** One side of a leaf of paper in a book: *For homework I had to read pages 17 and 18 in my science book.*

page² | pāj | —*noun, plural* **pages** A person who runs errands or delivers messages: *The page carried my message to my hotel room.* —*verb* **paged, paging** To call for someone in a public place: *When Tom got lost in the airport, his mother paged him on the loudspeaker.*

paint | pānt | —*noun, plural* **paints** Coloring matter mixed with oil or water: *John made a picture with 12 different colors of paint.* —*verb* **painted, painting** **1.** To cover or coat something with paint: *Alice painted her skateboard blue.* **2.** To make a picture using paint: *He liked to paint pictures of his dog, Igor.*

pair | pâr | —*noun, plural* **pairs** **I.** Two of a kind, usually used together: *Wendy bought a pair of sneakers for gym.* **2.** Two people or animals that go together: *A pair of white horses pulled the red wagon to the county fair.* • **Pair** sounds like **pear.**

pa·per | pā′pər | —*noun, plural* **papers** **I.** Material made from wood pulp, rags, etc. Paper is usually in the form of thin sheets. It is used for writing, drawing, printing, wrapping packages, and covering walls: *Tony used up all the paper in the house writing letters to his pen pal.* **2.** A newspaper: *I read about the parade in the paper.*

park | pärk | —*noun, plural* **parks** Land set aside for recreation by the people of a town or city: *Kathy and Kevin play in the park every Saturday.* —*verb* **parked, parking** To leave a vehicle in a certain spot: *We park our bikes in front of the school.*

part | pärt | —*noun, plural* **parts** **I.** Anything less than the whole: *Janie ate a part of Billy's sandwich.* **2.** A piece of something: *Parts of the model airplane were all over the table.* **3.** A role of a character in a play: *I got the part of the rabbit in the school play.*

par·ty | pär′tē | —*noun, plural* **parties** **I.** An entertainment or social gathering: *Jeff's friends gave him a surprise birthday party.* **2.** A group of people acting together: *A search party looked for the missing cat.*

pay | pā | —*verb* **paid, paying** **I.** To give money for something bought or for work done: *I had to pay 50 dollars for my new bicycle.* **2.** To give, or make, or do: *I always pay attention in dance class.* —*noun* Money given for work done: *My pay for raking the leaves was one dollar.*

pear | pâr | —*noun, plural* **pears** A sweet, juicy fruit, usually round at the bottom and pointed at the stem end: *I ate a pear.* • **Pear** sounds like **pair.**

pen·ny | pĕn′ē | —*noun, plural* **pennies** Onè cent: *When I've saved 100 pennies, I'll have one dollar.*

peo·ple | pē′pəl | —*noun, plural* **people** Human beings: *There were a lot of people at the party.*

place | plās | —*noun, plural* **places** A particular spot: *People travel from many places to see the rodeo.* —*verb* **placed, placing** To put in a particular spot or position: *I placed the toys on the shelf.*
  Idiom. **take place.** To happen: *I like to watch the fireworks take place on the Fourth of July.*

plant | plănt | *or* | plänt | —*noun, plural* **plants** Any form of vegetable life, such as trees, flowers, grass, etc.: *It's my job to water the plants in the classroom.* —*verb* **planted, planting** To put in the ground to grow: *My dad planted marigold seeds in the garden.*

please | plēz | —*verb* **pleased, pleasing** **I.** To give pleasure or happiness to; to be agreeable to: *He was pleased when I took him to the circus.* **2.** Be so kind as to: *Please close the door.*

point | point | —*noun, plural* **points** Sharp or narrowed end of something; the tip: *I broke the point on my pencil.* —*verb* **pointed, pointing** To call attention to with the finger; to show.

poor | pŏŏr | —*adjective* **poorer, poorest** **I.** Having little or no money: *She was too poor to go to the movies with her friends.* **2.** Needing pity: *The poor little mouse was afraid of the big cat.*

pop·corn | pŏp′kôrn′ | —*noun* A kind of corn that pops open and puffs up when heated: *I like watching popcorn pop almost as much as I like eating it.*

pour | pôr | *or* | pōr | —*verb* **poured, pouring** **1.** To cause to flow in a stream: *I always pour maple syrup over my pancakes.* **2.** A heavy rain: *We put up our umbrellas as it started to pour.*

pow·er | pou′ər | —*noun, plural* **powers** Strength or force: *A runner has plenty of power in her legs.*

pres·ent[1] | prĕz′ənt | —*noun* Now: *We seem happier in the present than in the past.*

pre·sent[2] | prĭ zĕnt′ | —*verb* **presented, presenting** To give as a gift: *John presented me with a medal after I won the race.* —*noun* | prĕz′ənt |, *plural* **presents** A gift: *My birthday present was a puppy.*

pret·ty | prĭt′ē | —*adjective* **prettier, prettiest** Pleasing; attractive; appealing: *The sunset was very pretty. That is the prettiest flower I ever saw.*

prob·lem | prŏb′ləm | —*noun, plural* **problems** A question that is hard to understand or settle: *Matt's problem was that his little sister followed him wherever he went.*

pull | po͝ol | —*verb* **pulled, pulling** To draw something toward oneself: *In a game of tug of war, you must pull on the rope as hard as you can.*

put | po͝ot | —*verb* **put, putting** To place; to set: *Allen put the cookies in the cookie jar.*

Q

quart | kwôrt | —*noun, plural* **quarts** **1.** Unit of measure equal to two pints or one quarter of a gallon: *I was so thirsty, I drank a quart of juice.* **2.** Container that holds a quart: *Jerry bought a quart of milk.*

queen | kwēn | —*noun, plural* **queens** **1.** A woman who rules over a country: *Queen Elizabeth is the ruler of England.* **2.** The wife of a king: *The king and the queen lived in a castle.*

qui·et | kwī′ĭt | —*adjective* **quieter, quietest** Silent; making little or no sound: *Laura was quiet so that she wouldn't wake her baby brother.*

R

rain | rān | —*noun* Drops of water that fall from the clouds: *The rain washed away Jan's sand castle.* —*verb* **rained, raining** To fall in drops of water from the clouds: *Ann didn't have to water the grass because it had rained all night.*

read | rēd | —*verb* **read** | rĕd |, **reading** To look at and get the meaning of something written or printed: *Every day I read the comics in the newspaper. I've already read the comics today.*

read·y | rĕd′ē | —*adjective* **readier, readiest** Prepared to do something: *Doris was packed and ready to go.*

re·al | rē′əl | *or* | rēl | —*adjective* Actual; true; not made up: *Is that a real diamond?*

re·turn | rĭ tûrn′ | —*verb* **returned, returning** **1.** To come or go back: *Every summer I can't wait to return to our cabin at the lake.* **2.** To give back: *Tom forgot to return his library books.*

right | rīt | —*adjective* **1.** Opposite the left side: *I throw a ball with my right* arm. **2.** Correct; true; just: *Telling the truth is the right thing to do.* —*adverb* Straight on; directly: *I turned around without looking and walked right into a wall.* • **Right** sounds like **write**.

riv·er | rĭv′ər | —*noun, plural* **rivers** A large stream of water that flows into a lake, ocean, sea, or another river: *My dad and I go fishing in the river.*

road | rōd | —*noun, plural* **roads** An open way for travel between two or more places: *Do you remember how Dorothy followed the yellow brick road to Oz?*

rock | rŏk | —*noun, plural* **rocks** Solid stone: *The trail was covered with rocks.*

roy·al | roi′əl | —*adjective* **1.** Of or having to do with kings or queens: *The prince was a member of the royal family.* **2.** Fit for a king or queen; splendid: *The queen lived in a royal palace.*

S

safe | sāf | —*adjective* **safer, safest** Free from danger or harm: *Police officers help make the streets safe.*

said | sĕd | Look up **say**.

sail | sāl | —*noun, plural* **sails** A piece of strong material spread to catch the wind and make a boat move: *As the wind filled the sails, the sailboat moved faster.* —*verb* **sailed, sailing** **1.** To travel across water on a ship: *The ship is going to sail across the ocean to Europe.* **2.** To steer a boat: *I sailed the boat across the lake all by myself.*

Sat·ur·day | săt′ər dē | *or* | săt′ər dā′ | —*noun, plural* **Saturdays** The seventh day of the week: *Mom took us to the baseball game on Saturday.*

save | sāv | —*verb* **saved, saving** **1.** To free from danger or harm: *Marie saved Ellen from falling off the swing.* **2.** To avoid wasting: *I took the bus instead of walking to save time.*

say | sā | —*verb* **says** | sĕz |, **said** | sĕd |, **saying** To speak; to talk: *Grandma says it's time for dinner.*

school[1] | skōol | —*noun, plural* **schools** A place of teaching and learning: *We learned about Japan in school.*

school[2] | skōol | —*noun, plural* **schools** A large group of fish that swim together: *While we were fishing, a school of guppies swam by.*

sea | sē | —*noun, plural* **seas** The great body of water that covers about three-fourths of the earth's surface; ocean: *Whales live in the sea.*

sec·ond[1] | sĕk′ənd | —*noun, plural* **seconds** A unit of time equal to 1/60 of one minute: *Janet finished the test in 3 minutes and 10 seconds flat.*

sec·ond[2] | sĕk′ənd | —*adjective* Next after the first: *Mike came in first in the race, and I came in second.*

send | sĕnd | —*verb* **sent** | sĕnt |, **sending** To cause or order to go: *Dad sent me to the store to buy ice cream for dessert.*

sent | sĕnt | Look up **send**. • **Sent** sounds like **cent**.

Sep·tem·ber | sĕp tĕm′bər | —*noun* The ninth month of the year. September has 30 days: *In September we go back to school.*

shake | shāk | —*verb* **shook** | shŏok |, **shaken, shaking** **1.** To tremble or quiver: *I was so scared, my whole body began to shake.* **2.** To cause to move: *The boys shook the tree, and all the leaves fell off.*

sharp | shärp | —*adjective* **sharper, sharpest** **1.** Something having a thin, cutting edge or point: *Anna needed a sharper knife to cut her tough steak.* **2.** Quickly aware of things; keen: *Owls' sharp eyesight helps them to see in the dark.*

she'd | shēd | The contraction of "she had" or "she would": *She'd already seen the movie. Donna said she'd go to the store with me.*

she'll | shēl | The contraction of "she will": *My mother says she'll pick us up after practice.*

she's | shēz | The contraction of "she is" or "she has": *Molly says she's going to swim across the lake, but she's never done it before.*

shine | shīn | —*verb* **shone** | shōn | or **shined, shining** **1.** To give off or reflect light: *Stop shining that flashlight at me.* **2.** To polish: *I polished my shoes until they shone.*

shirt | shûrt | —*noun, plural* **shirts** Clothing for the upper part of the body. A shirt usually has a collar and sleeves: *The team always wore blue shirts when they played football.*

shook | shŏok | Look up **shake.**

shop | shŏp | —*noun, plural* **shops** A store; a place where goods are sold: *Don's favorite shop is Happy's Toy Store.* —*verb* **shopped, shopping** To visit stores to buy things: *My brother and I went shopping for a pet frog.*

should | shŏod | —*helping* or *auxiliary verb* Ought to; have a duty to: *I should practice the piano every day.*

should·n't | shŏod′nt | The contraction of "should not": *You shouldn't pull a cat's tail because you might hurt the cat.*

shove | shŭv | —*verb* **shoved, shoving** To push roughly: *When Mom came into my room, I shoved her present under the bed.* —*noun, plural* **shoves** A push: *My dog wouldn't move so I gave him a little shove.*

show | shō | —*verb* **showed, showed** or **shown, showing** **1.** To make known; to reveal: *It shows on my face when I'm sad.* **2.** To place in sight: *Let's show everyone our bowling trophy.* —*noun, plural* **shows** Any kind of public performance, entertainment, or display: *Ms. Cook's class put on an art show for the school.*

side | sīd | —*noun, plural* **sides** One of the surfaces of an object: *This jack-in-the-box has four sides and a top and bottom.*

size | sīz | —*noun, plural* **sizes** The height, width, or length of a thing: *The twins, Billy and Barry, have always been the same size.*

sky | skī | —*noun, plural* **skies** The air high above the earth; the heavens: *I fly my kite high in the sky.*

sleep | slēp | —*noun* A natural rest of body and mind; state of not being awake: *I'm so tired, I could use a week of sleep.* —*verb* **slept, sleeping** To be in or to fall into a state of sleep: *The bear slept in his den all winter.*

sleep·y | slē′pē | —*adjective* **sleepier, sleepiest** Ready for sleep; drowsy: *When I am sleepy, I start to yawn.*

slow | slō | —*adverb* **slower, slowest** Not quick: *Bobby walks slower than a turtle.* —*verb* **slowed, slowing** To cause to move slow or slower: *I stepped on the brakes to slow down my bike.*

smile | smīl | —*noun, plural* **smiles** Upward curve of the mouth to show

happiness: *Dad wanted to see a smile on my face before he took my picture.*
—*verb* **smiled, smiling** The act of smiling: *Jenny smiled at the animals.*

sneeze | snēz | —*verb* **sneezed, sneezing** To force air to pass suddenly with force from the nose and mouth. A tickling feeling inside the nose causes a person to sneeze: *When John caught a cold, he sneezed for two days.*

snow | snō | —*noun, plural* **snows** Soft white flakes of frozen water vapor that form in the sky and fall to the earth: *Jeremy loved to ride his sled in the snow.* —*verb* **snowed, snowing** To fall as snow: *When it stopped snowing, I had to shovel the walk.*

sock | sŏk | —*noun, plural* **socks** A short stocking reaching no higher than the knee: *I stepped in a puddle and got my shoes and socks soaked.*

soft | sôft | *or* | sŏft | —*adjective* **softer, softest** **1.** Not hard: *My pillow is as soft as cotton.* **2.** Not loud: *Speak in a soft voice, or you'll wake your brother.*

soil¹ | soil | —*noun, plural* **soils** The loose top layer of the earth's surface in which plants grow: *My class planted a little tree in the soil.*

soil² | soil | —*verb* **soiled, soiling** To make dirty: *Jane soiled her clean shirt.*

some | sŭm | —*adjective* A few; a little: *Some people like pizza, and some people don't.* • **Some** sounds like **sum.**

some·one | sŭm′wŭn′ | *or* | sŭm′wən | —*pronoun* Some unknown person; somebody: *I hope someone finds my lost dog and returns her.*

some·thing | sŭm′thĭng | —*pronoun* A particular thing that is not named or known: *I want something to eat, but I don't know what.*

son | sŭn | —*noun, plural* **sons** A male child: *My parents have three daughters, but I am their only son.* • **Son** sounds like **sun.**

sor·ry | sŏr′ē | *or* | sôr′ē | —*adjective* **sorrier, sorriest** Feeling sadness, regret, or pity: *Susy was sorry that she lost her sister's record.*

sound | sound | —*noun, plural* **sounds** Something that is heard; sensation made by vibrations in the air and picked up by the ear: *We were surprised to hear thumping sounds coming from the empty attic.*

speed | spēd | —*noun, plural* **speeds** To move rapidly or quickly: *The dog chased the cat down the street with great speed.* —*verb* **sped** *or* **speeded, speeding** To cause to move at a faster rate: *I went speeding down the hill on my roller skates.*

spend | spĕnd | —*verb* **spent** | spĕnt |, **spending** **1.** To pay out money: *He spent a lot of money for a new bat.* **2.** To pass time: *Katy spent the whole day at the carnival.*

spent | spĕnt | Look up **spend.**

spoil | spoil | —*verb* **spoiled** *or* **spoilt, spoiling** **1.** To ruin or damage: *The rain spoiled the class picnic.* **2.** To become unfit for use: *The milk will spoil if you forget to keep it cold.*

sport | spôrt | *or* | spōrt | —*noun, plural* **sports** A game or contest requiring physical activity: *My favorite sport is soccer.*

spring | sprĭng | —*noun, plural* **springs** **1.** The season between winter and summer: *In the spring the flowers start to bloom.* **2.** A place where water flows to the surface of the ground: *We went for a swim in the spring.*

stair | stâr | —*noun, plural* **stairs** A step in a flight of steps: *Tommy climbed the stairs to his room.*

stand | stănd | —*verb* **stood** | sto͝od |, **standing** To rise to the feet: *The lion stood on the mountain top.*

star | stär | —*noun, plural* **stars** **1.** Any heavenly body, other than the moon or planets, seen from Earth in the night sky: *The best part of camping is watching the stars at night.* **2.** A famous person in any field or profession: *Who is your favorite movie star?*

start | stärt | —*verb* **started, starting** To begin to go somewhere or do something: *Let's start a fan club.*

state | stāt | —*noun, plural* **states** A political unit; a government: *There are 50 states in the United States of America.* —*verb* **stated, stating** To say clearly in words: *Bob stated that he was very hungry.*

still | stĭl | —*adjective* **stiller, stillest** Quiet: *The class was still before the test.* —*adverb* **1.** Not moving: *The cat could sit still for hours.* **2.** Even; yet: *I still don't have enough money to buy new skates.*

stood | sto͝od | Look up **stand.**

stop | stŏp | —*verb* **stopped, stopping** To cease; to come to a halt: *When the rain stopped, Steven went out to play.*

storm | stôrm | —*noun, plural* **storms** Strong winds accompanied by rain, hail, sand, or snow: *The storm blew down a big tree.*

sto·ry | stôr′ē | *or* | stōr′ē | —*noun, plural* **stories** **1.** An account of something that has happened: *Did you read the story?* **2.** A tale of fiction: *Phil tells his sister a bedtime story before she goes to sleep.*

street | strēt | —*noun, plural* **streets** A road in a city or town that is usually lined with buildings: *My house is on the same street as yours.*

strong | strông | *or* | strŏng | —*adjective* **stronger, strongest** Having much power or strength: *John Henry was strong enough to beat the steam drill.*

sub·tract | səb trăkt′ | —*verb* **subtracted, subtracting** To take away: *Subtract two cents from eights cents, and you'll have six cents.*

such | sŭch | —*adjective* Of this kind or that kind: *I didn't know you would wear such shoes.* —*adverb* Especially: *That was such a nice party.*

sum | sŭm | —*noun, plural* **sums** The number you get when you add two or more numbers: *The sum of 5 cookies and 6 cookies is 11 cookies.* • **Sum** sounds like **some.**

sum·mer | sŭm′ər | —*noun, plural* **summers** The warmest season of the year. Summer comes between spring and fall: *Tim goes to camp every summer.*

sun | sŭn | —*noun* The star around which the Earth and other planets revolve. The sun is the source of light and heat: *I wake up when the sun rises in the morning.* • **Sun** sounds like **son.**

Sun·day | sŭn′dē | *or* | sŭn′dā′ | —*noun, plural* **Sundays** The first day of the week: *On Sunday Inga went to church.*

sun·ny | sŭn′ē | —*adjective* Having much sun: *It was a sunny day at the beach.*

sup·per | sŭp′ər | —*noun, plural* **suppers** The evening meal or the last meal of the day: *My family ate supper at a restaurant last night.*

sure | sho͝or | —*adjective* **surer, surest** Feeling certain; having no doubt: *Are you sure you don't want a piece of cake?*

T

ta·ble | tā′bəl | —*noun, plural* **tables** A piece of furniture having a flat top supported by legs: *Dinner was already on the table when I got home.*

take | tāk | —*verb* **took** | tŏok |, **taken, taking** **1.** To get; accept: *Mike took the award for the whole team.* **2.** To carry to a different place: *I am taking your suitcase upstairs.* **3.** To move; remove: *Claire took her watch off her hand.*

talk | tôk | —*verb* **talked, talking** To speak; utter words: *We were talking about Mark, when he walked in.* —*noun* **1.** An informal speech: *I gave a talk in science class.* **2.** A rumor; gossip: *There was talk that school would be closed tomorrow because of the snow.*

tall | tôl | —*adjective* **taller, tallest** **1.** Of more than average height: *Ben is five inches taller than I am.* **2.** Hard to believe; exaggerated: *Who would believe that tall story?*

team | tēm | —*noun, plural* **teams** **1.** Two or more animals harnessed together to work: *Dad used a team of horses to plow the field.* **2.** A group of people playing on the same side in a game: *The whole school came to watch our baseball team win.*

tell | tĕl | —*verb* **told** | tōld |, **telling** To put into words; to say: *I told Dad what had happened at school today.*

test | tĕst | —*noun, plural* **tests** **1.** A series of questions that judge a person's skill or knowledge: *I studied hard to pass my spelling test.* **2.** A way to find out the quality of something: *Lifting weights will test how strong you are.* —*verb* **tested, testing** To put to a test; to try out: *I tested the yo-yo to make sure it worked before I bought it.*

thank | thăngk | —*verb* **thanked, thanking** To say that one is grateful or pleased: *The boys and girls thanked the magician for the show.*

them | thĕm | —*pronoun* Persons, things, or animals spoken or written about: *After Connie made the peanut butter cookies, she put them in the cookie jar.*

then | thĕn | —*adverb* **1.** At the time: *I used to sleep with a teddy bear, but I was only a kid then.* **2.** After that: *We saw lightning flash and then we heard the thunder roar.* **3.** A time mentioned: *Go finish your homework and by then dinner will be ready.*

these | thēz | Look up **this.**

they | thā | —*pronoun* **1.** The people, animals, or things named before: *Mr. Martin gave us six arithmetic problems, and they were all hard.* **2.** People in general: *They used to think the world was flat.*

they'd | thād | The contraction of "they had" or "they would": *I asked Don and Bill if they'd seen my cat anywhere. Don and Bill said they'd treat me to an ice cream cone.*

they'll | thāl | The contraction of "they will" or "they shall": *Arnold and Bonnie said they'll bring the cake to the party.*

they've | thāv | The contraction of "they have": *The twins say they've never gone fishing.*

thing | thĭng | —*noun, plural* **things** **1.** Any object or substance that cannot be named exactly: *What is that green thing on the floor?* **2.** An act; a deed: *Hitting that home run was the best thing I ever did.*

think | thĭngk | —*verb* **thought, thinking**
1. To use the mind to come to an opinion: *I think I should go home now.*
2. To have in mind: *Julia thinks she would like to be a doctor.*

third | thûrd | —*noun, plural* **thirds** One of three equal parts: *Roger ate a third of the pizza.* —*adjective* Next after second: *Alice was the third person in line for the concert.*

this | thĭs | —*adjective, plural* **these** | thēz | Referring to a thing or person nearby or just mentioned: *Move these toys before you trip over them.* —*pronoun, plural* **these** A thing or person nearby or just mentioned: *This is our secret clubhouse.*

Thurs·day | thûrz′dē | *or* | thûrz′dā′ | —*noun, plural* **Thursdays** The fifth day of the week: *Art class meets every Thursday after school.*

times | tīmz | —*preposition* Multiplied by: *Three times two equals six.*

ti·ny | tī′nē | —*adjective* **tinier, tiniest** Very small: *The kitten was so tiny, it fit in my hand.*

tire[1] | tīr | —*verb* **tired, tiring** To become weary: *Millie tired after hiking all day.*

tire[2] | tīr | —*noun, plural* **tires** A band of rubber around the rim of a wheel: *My bicycle has a flat tire.*

toast | tōst | —*verb* **toasted, toasting** To brown by heating: *We toasted marshmallows over the campfire.* —*noun* A slice of bread heated and browned on both sides: *I always have toast with my breakfast.*

toe | tō | —*noun, plural* **toes** One of the five separate divisions of the foot: *Ellen put her big toe into the bath water to see if it was too hot.*

told | tōld | Look up **tell.**

too | tōō | —*adverb* 1. Also; besides: *Adam had to make the salad and set the table, too.* 2. Very: *This soup is too hot to eat.* • **Too** sounds like **two.**

took | tŏŏk | Look up **take.**

tooth | tōōth | —*noun, plural* **teeth** Any of the hard, white, bony parts in the mouth used for biting and chewing: *Judy's front tooth is ready to fall out.*

tow·er | tou′ər | —*noun, plural* **towers** A high structure or a part of a building rising higher than the rest of it: *Rapunzel was hidden away in a tower so that no one could reach her.*

town | toun | —*noun, plural* **towns** A group of houses or buildings that is larger than a village but smaller than a city: *My aunt is the new mayor of our town.*

toy | toi | —*noun, plural* **toys** Something a child plays with: *Johnny's favorite toy is Robbie-the-Robot.*

train | trān | —*noun, plural* **trains** Connected railroad cars pulled by an engine or powered by electricity: *Mom and I went by train to visit Aunt Bess.*

truck | trŭk | —*noun, plural* **trucks** A large vehicle used for carrying heavy loads: *When the Fishers moved, they sent all their furniture by truck.*

true | trōō | —*adjective* **truer, truest** Not false; according to fact: *Only June knows the true story.*

try | trī | —*verb* **tried, trying, tries** To make an effort; to attempt: *Will you try to cheer up Debbie?*

Tues·day | tōōz′dē | *or* | tōōz′dā′ | *or* | tyōōz′dē | *or* | tyōōz′dā′ | —*noun, plural* **Tuesdays** The third day of the week: *I go to the library every Tuesday.*

turn | tûrn | —*verb* **turned, turning**
1. To move round; rotate: *The Earth*

turns on its axis once every 24 hours.
2. To change direction or position: *The path turned into the woods.* —*noun, plural* **turns** A chance to do something after someone else: *Finally, it was Jenny's turn at bat.*

two | tōō | —*noun* One more than one: *The twins are two of my good buddies.*
• **Two** sounds like **too.**

U

un·der | ŭn′dər | —*preposition* **1.** Below; beneath: *I put my shoes under my bed.* **2.** Less than: *Sue was under 12, so she went to the movies for half-price.*

use | yōōz | —*verb* **used, using** To put into service: *I used the whole day to finish my science project.*
Idiom. **used to.** Familiar with: *I was used to sleeping with the light on.*

used | yōōzd | —*adjective* Not new: *Nick bought a used bike.*

V

ver·y | vĕr′ē | —*adverb* Much; extremely: *That joke was very funny.*

voice | vois | —*noun, plural* **voices** The sound coming from the mouth: *Bernice has a wonderful voice.*

W

wait | wāt | —*verb* **waited, waiting** To stay until someone comes or something

happens: *We could hardly wait for the cartoon to start.* • **Wait** sounds like **weight.**

walk | wôk | —*verb* **walked, walking** To go on foot at a steady pace: *The elephant walked slowly around the big circus tent.*

want | wŏnt | *or* | wônt | —*verb* **wanted, wanting** To wish for; desire: *I want a pogo stick for my birthday.*

was | wŏz | *or* | wŭz | *or* | wəz | Look up **be.**

wash | wŏsh | *or* | wôsh | —*verb* **washed, washing** To clean with a liquid, usually water: *I'll wash if you dry.*

was·n't | wŏz′ənt | *or* | wŭz′ənt | The contraction of "was not": *Bill wasn't ready when his friends arrived.*

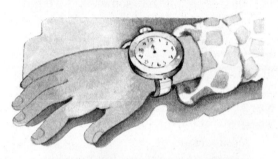

watch | wŏch | —*verb* **watched, watching** To look carefully or to look at: *My family and I watched the Thanksgiving parade from the sidewalk.* —*noun, plural* **watches** A small clock carried in a pocket or worn on the wrist: *According to my watch, it's time for lunch.*

wa·ter | wô′tər | *or* | wŏt′ər | —*noun* **1.** The colorless, tasteless, odorless liquid that fills oceans, rivers, and ponds: *Water falls from the sky as rain.* **2.** A lake, river, pool, or any other body of this liquid: *We went for a swim in the water.* —*verb* **watered, watering** To sprinkle or provide with water: *The rain watered the grass for me.*

we'd | wēd | The contraction of "we had," "we should," or "we would": *We'd better go home before it gets too late. We'd love to take the kitten, but we already have three cats.*

Wed·nes·day | wĕnz′dē | *or* | wĕnz′dā′ | —*noun, plural* **Wednesdays** The fourth day of the week: *We have cooking class on Wednesday.*

weigh | wā | —*verb* **weighed, weighing**
1. To find out how heavy something is by using a scale: *Mom lets me weigh the vegetables before she buys them.* **2.** To have a certain weight: *Jason's dog, Mimi, weighs only 11 pounds.*

weight | wāt | —*noun, plural* **weights** The amount that something weighs: *The baby's weight went up each week.*
• **Weight** sounds like **wait.**

we'll | wĕl | The contraction of "we will" or "we shall": *We'll go into the Fun House with you.*

were | wûr | Look up **be.**

were·n't | wûrnt | *or* | **wûr′**ənt | The contraction of "were not": *My friends weren't home when I stopped by.*

we've | wēv | The contraction of "we have": *We've still got a lot of work to do on the tree house.*

what | hwŏt | *or* | hwŭt | *or* | wŏt | *or* | wŭt | *or* | hwət | *or* | wət | —*pronoun* **1.** Which thing or things: *What do you want me to do?* **2.** The thing which: *She didn't know what her mother would say about her report card.* **3.** Which: *What color do you want to paint your room?*

wheel | hwēl | *or* | wēl | —*noun, plural* **wheels** A round frame supported by spokes on which a vehicle moves: *Have you ever been on the Ferris wheel?*

when | hwĕn | *or* | wĕn | —*adverb* **1.** At what time: *When will you be ready to go?* **2.** At a particular time: *I'll call you when I get to Aunt Sara's house.*

where | hwâr | *or* | wâr | —*adverb* **1.** At what place: *Where are my mittens?* **2.** To what place: *Where are we going on our class trip?*

which | hwĭch | *or* | wĭch | —*pronoun* **1.** What one or ones: *Which is my ice cream cone?* **2.** That: *I bought my mother a present, which I know she will like.* —*adjective* What one or ones: *Pam couldn't tell which cowboy hat was hers.*

while | hwīl | *or* | wīl | —*noun* A period of time: *Please stay for a while.* —*conjunction* **1.** At the same time that: *Mom read the newspaper while I did my homework.* **2.** Although: *Ron was short while his brothers were tall.*

white | hwīt | *or* | wīt | —*noun* The lightest color; the color of snow: *White is the color of the clouds on a sunny day.* —*adjective* **whiter, whitest** Having the color white: *I have white shoes.*

who | hoō | —*pronoun* What person or persons: *Who is your best friend?*

whole | hōl | —*adjective* **1.** Not broken; complete: *Is this a whole deck of cards?* **2.** Entire amount: *I ate the whole pie by myself.* • **Whole** sounds like **hole.**

why | hwī | *or* | wī | —*adverb* For what reason: *Why is your tongue green?*

wide | wīd | —*adjective* **wider, widest** Extending over a large area; broad: *The river was so wide that they built a bridge across it.*

wild | wīld | —*adjective* **wilder, wildest** Living or growing in a natural state: *We ate wild berries on our camping trip.*

will | wĭl | —*helping* or *auxiliary verb* Intention: *I will go to the class picnic.*

win | wĭn | —*verb* **won** | wŭn |, **winning** To gain a victory: *Who won the Ping-Pong contest?*

win·ter | wĭn′tər | —*noun, plural* **winters** The coldest season of the year, coming between fall and spring: *I don't like to shovel snow in the winter.*

wire | wīr | —*noun, plural* **wires** Metal drawn out into a thin thread: *The fence around the farm was made of wire.*

wish | wĭsh | —*noun, plural* **wishes** A strong desire: *Renee's only wish was to be finished with her work.* —*verb* **wished, wishing** To have a desire for something: *Ken wished he could meet his favorite singing star.*

won | wŭn | Look up **win.**

won't | wōnt | The contraction of "will not": *I won't be at the park today.*

wood | wŏŏd | —*noun* The hard material making up the trunk and branches of a tree: *The cabin was built of wood.*
• **Wood** sounds like **would.**

word | wûrd | —*noun, plural* **words** A sound or group of sounds having a certain meaning: *I missed only one word on my spelling test.*

work | wûrk | —*noun* **I.** The effort made in doing or making something: *Mowing the lawn is hard work.* **2.** A task: *I can't go because I have too much school work to do.* —*verb* **worked, working** To have a job: *Joe worked at the supermarket after school.*

world | wûrld | —*noun* The Earth: *In history class we learn about the world.*

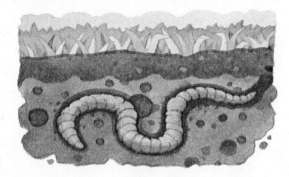

worm | wûrm | —*noun, plural* **worms** A crawling creature with a long, slender body: *There are lots of worms in the backyard.*

would | wŏŏd | —*helping* or *auxiliary verb* Past tense of **will,** meaning was or were intending to: *I knew you would come sooner or later.* • **Would** sounds like **wood.**

would·n't | wŏŏd'nt | The contraction of "would not": *Sam knew he wouldn't get home on time unless he ran.*

write | rīt | —*verb* **wrote** | rōt |, **written, writing** To make letters or words with a pen, pencil, etc.: *Karen promised to*

write to me when she went on vacation. I wrote to my sister from my aunt's.

wrote | rōt | Look up **write.**

yard¹ | yärd | —*noun, plural* **yards** A unit of length measuring 3 feet or 36 inches: *This room is three yards long.*

yard² | yärd | —*noun, plural* **yards** A piece of land near a building: *At lunch time we get to play in the school yard.*

year | yîr | —*noun, plural* **years** The length of time it takes the Earth to go around the sun once; 365 days: *This year I will be 10 years old.*

yel·low | yĕl'ō | —*noun* The color of gold or butter: *Yellow is the color of ripe lemons.* —*adjective* **yellower, yellowest** Having this color: *I wore my yellow shirt with my blue pants.*

you'd | yōŏd | The contraction of "you had" or "you would": *You'd better go to bed before you fall asleep in the chair. I know that you'd really like to join our club.*

you'll | yōŏl | The contraction of "you will" or "you shall": *You broke this vase, so you'll have to pay for it.*

your | yŏŏr | *or* | yôr | *or* | yōr | *or* | yər | —*pronoun* Of or belonging to you: *Your hat is on the floor.*

your·self | yŏŏr **sĕlf'** | *or* | yôr **sĕlf'** | *or* | yōr **sĕlf'** | *or* | yər **sĕlf'** | —*pronoun, plural* **yourselves** Your own person: *Can you carry that box yourself?*

you've | yōŏv | The contraction of "you have": *You've got a turtle just like mine.*

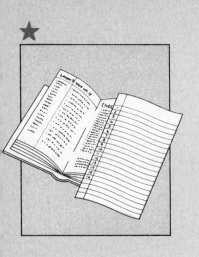

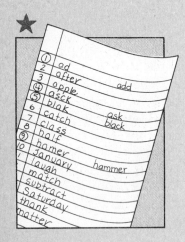

THE CHECKPOINT
Study Plan

When you have finished a Checkpoint page and you know that you have the correct answers, use the Checkpoint page and this Study Plan to test yourself.

★ Cover your answers to the Checkpoint page with a piece of paper. Number the paper 1 through 16. For each spelling clue, do steps 1, 2, and 3.

1 Read the clue and say the answer.

2 Spell the answer aloud.

3 Write the answer

★ Uncover your first answers and do steps 4, 5, and 6.

4 Check your answers.

5 Circle the number of each misspelled word.

6 Write the correct spelling next to each incorrect word.

★ To study, cover your answers again, and fold the paper so that only the numbers show. For each circled number, repeat steps 1 through 6.